The Ages of
the Earth

FOUNDATIONS OF SCIENCE LIBRARY

The Natural World
(4 volumes)

The Majesty of the Heavens
(Foundations of Astronomy)

The Round World
(Foundations of Geology and Geomorphology)

The Skies and the Seas
(Foundations of Meteorology, Oceanography & Cartography)

The Ages of the Earth
(Foundations of Palaeogeography and Palaeontology)

The Biological Sciences
(6 volumes)

The Life of Animals without Backbones
(Foundations of Invertebrate Zoology)

The Life of Animals with Backbones
(Foundations of Vertebrate Zoology)

The World of Plants
(Foundations of Botany)

Breeding and Growing
(Foundations of Genetics, Anthropology and Agriculture)

Patterns of Living
(Foundations of Ecology)

Human Kind
(Foundations of Human Biology)

The Physical Sciences
(9 volumes)

The Restlessness of Matter
(Foundations of Aerodynamics, Hydrodynamics and Thermodynamics)

The Science of Movement
(Foundations of Mechanics and Sound)

Lightning in Harness
(Foundations of Electricity)

The Silent Energy
(Foundations of Electrical Technology)

The Cathode Ray Revolution
(Foundations of Electronics)

The Rays of Light
(Foundations of Optics)

The Unseen Spectrum
(Foundations of Electromagnetic Radiation)

The Cosmic Power
(Foundations of Nuclear Physics)

The Discipline of Numbers
(Foundations of Mathematics)

The Chemical Sciences
(4 volumes)

The Fundamental Materials
(Foundations of Basic Chemistry)

The Elements and their Order
(Foundations of Inorganic Chemistry)

The Giant Molecules
(Foundations of Organic Chemistry)

The Chemist at Work
(Foundations of Analysis and Laboratory Techniques)

Technology
(5 volumes)

The Metallic Skills
(Foundations of Metallurgy)

Industrial Processing
(Foundations of Industrial and Chemical Technology)

Engineering Technology
(Foundations of Applied Engineering)

Automobile Engineering
(Foundations of Car Mechanics)

The Inventive Genius
(Foundations of Scientific Inventions)

History and Reference
(3 volumes)

The Beginnings of Science
(Foundations of Scientific History)

Frontiers of Science
(Foundations of Research Methods)

A Dictionary of Scientific Terms
(The Foundations of Science Reference Book)

CHIEF EDITORS

Leslie Basford, B.Sc.   Philip Kogan, M.Sc.

ASSISTANT EDITORS

Michael Dempsey, B.A., Michael Gabb, B.Sc., Clare Dover, B.Sc.
Cyril Parsons, B.Sc., Joan Pick, B.Sc., Michael Chinery, B.A.
David Larkin, B.Sc., Paul Drury Byrne, B.Sc.

CONSULTANT EDITORIAL BOARD

Sir Lawrence Bragg, M.C., O.B.E., F.R.S., M.A., Nobel Laureate

Sir James Chadwick, F.R.S., Ph.D., M.Sc., Nobel Laureate

Norman Fisher, M.A.

Sir Harry Melville, K.C.B., F.R.S., Ph.D., D.Sc.

Professor J. Z. Young, F.R.S., M.A.

The Ages of the Earth

Foundations of Palaeogeography and Palaeontology

MICHAEL DEMPSEY, B.A.   DAVID LARKIN, B.Sc.

FOUNDATIONS OF SCIENCE LIBRARY

THE NATURAL WORLD

DISTRIBUTED IN THE U.S.A. BY
Ginn and Company : BOSTON
PUBLISHED BY
Sampson Low, Marston and Co : LONDON

This new presentation assembles
freshly edited material from
'Understanding Science' on one
subject into a single volume.

Copyright © 1966 Sampson Low, Marston & Co. Ltd.

Library of Congress Catalog Card
Number: 66–17991

Catalog No: L–20665

Made and printed in Great Britain by
Purnell & Sons Ltd., Paulton
(Somerset) and London

PALAEOGEOGRAPHY
AND PALAEONTOLOGY

Contents

The Key
to the Past

CHAPTER ONE

What are Fossils?

FOSSILS are traces of animals or plants which have been naturally preserved in various ways, sometimes for many millions of years.

Many millions of years ago an ichthyosaur died and sank to the bottom of the sea. In time its skeleton was covered with mud, which gradually settled into solid rock layers. The encased skeleton was then gradually fossilized. At a much later date earth movements buckled the sea bed which consequently rose to become dry land. Then erosion by ice, water and wind slowly stripped off the rock, thus uncovering the fossilized skeleton.

When an animal dies its body usually decomposes or is eaten by other animals. But the hard parts, the shell or bones and teeth, are not so easy to destroy. The essential conditions needed for preservation are that the animal should be buried relatively quickly, i.e. before the elements have time to reduce the bones to dust, and that the rock in which it occurs should escape metamorphism (change by heat or pressure). The best conditions for preservation exist in the sea, especially near the coast, which is the reason why nearly all fossils are found in sedimentary rocks. Even fossils of land animals have been found in such rocks, probably through having been swept out to sea in floods.

Fossils take on a number of different forms. Very occasionally the actual skeleton may be preserved. This has happened where animals have been trapped in bogs or tar pits and quickly buried. The Californian tar pits, for instance, have yielded a wealth of skeletal remains. And under very unusual conditions the entire animal may be preserved. Mammoths (the forerunners of present-day elephants) have been found in Alaska and Siberia preserved almost intact in ice.

More often, however, the buried skeletons are petrified, i.e. replaced by stone. This is caused by ground water depositing mineral matter in the pores of the bones, a process known as *permineralization*. On the other hand, each particle of the substance may be eaten away and *replaced* by a particle of mineral matter. Petrified bones are usually produced by the former process and petrified wood by the latter.

Some buried substances may be completely eaten away by percolating ground water, leaving a space in the rock corresponding to the original form of the object. This is known as a *mould*. Ground water may later fill this cavity with mineral matter, thus producing a rock *cast* of the object. Interesting moulds have been formed by insects becoming trapped in resin dripping from evergreen trees. This gradually hardens to form amber, and although most of the insect dries and withers away, the outline of its original form can clearly be seen from the hollow in the transparent material. Moulds of extremely thin objects, such as leaves, are generally spoken of as *imprints*.

Many plant fossils are simply residues of carbon which give the actual shape of the original object, and fossils of soft-bodied invertebrate animals are occasionally formed in this way too. Sometimes the petrified skeleton of an animal may be surrounded by a film of carbon which shows the actual fleshy outline of the creature as it was.

Unusual fossils are the tracks left by animals in mud which later hardened to become rock. Excellent dinosaur footprints, for instance, have been found by the side of an old water course in the Gobi Desert of Central Asia and in many other areas.

Fossils are a key to the past. They help to explain the changing pattern of life through the ages. But dating them can be difficult. Take, for example, a 100-foot-high chalk cliff. Geologists have calculated that it took 30,000 years for each foot of chalk to form. Thus a fossil found 30 feet above another would be 900,000 years younger than the one below. But this only gives their *relative* ages. Their actual age cannot be determined until the actual age of the chalk has been determined.

How are fossils found?

Fossils have often been unearthed in mines, quarries and other excavations, even by ploughing; but they have been exposed most frequently as water, wind and ice wears away the land.

People out for walks may pick them up at the foot of cliffs, or in quarries or in fields. Often they keep them as ornaments, not realizing that they are the remains of an animal or plant that lived perhaps many millions of years ago. Sometimes these 'ornaments' find their way into museums where they are identified.

More usually, however, fossils are found today as the result of systematic searching by trained fossil hunters. As the result of years of experience palaeontologists (people who study fossils) know which rocks are likely to contain certain fossils and where these rocks are to be found. Sites are marked off so that the position of any

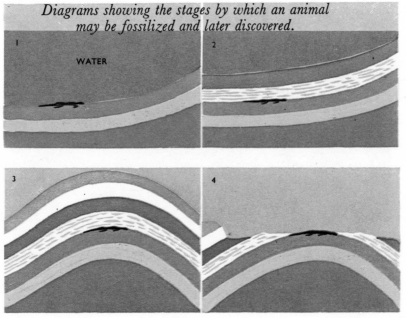

Diagrams showing the stages by which an animal may be fossilized and later discovered.

WATER

The Morrison formation (Rocky Mountain region, U.S.A.) is rich in fossils of many different kinds of animals, particularly dinosaurs. It resulted from the deposition of river-borne sand, gravel, and mud. When this was happening, perhaps 140,000,000 years ago, the region was a low-lying plain, covered with luxuriant vegetation and crossed by many sluggish streams and rivers.

A film of carbon shows the original outline of this ichthyosaur body.

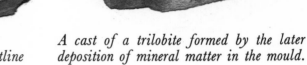

A cast of a trilobite formed by the later deposition of mineral matter in the mould.

finds can be located.

Once a large fossil has been found, the task of unearthing it, covering it in a protective coat of plaster for its journey to the museum, and cleaning, repairing and piecing the bones together again may take a considerable amount of time.

Looking for Fossils

The rocks containing fossils are of three main types, sandstones which are gritty, shales which are softer and more plastic, and limestones which are usually hard. Sandstones are generally poor for fossil hunting. They are porous and water can easily penetrate and dissolve away the minerals making the fossils. What fossils are found, are usually fragile. They should be gently treated and carried in small boxes filled with cottonwool or other shock-absorbent material.

Shales are more rewarding, though sticky and unpleasant to work in. They are made of fine-grained clay minerals and are not porous. Water cannot percolate freely and the hard remains of buried organisms are not dissolved. Unfortunately shales are easily compressed and tend to shrink. Often this shrinkage causes the fossils to be squashed and flattened.

A mould of a trilobite, the impression that may remain after the actual animal has disappeared.

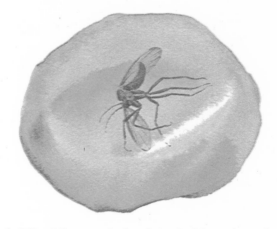

The Oligocene beds of the Baltic region of Germany have yielded good examples of insects encased in amber.

One of the best examples of petrified wood occurs in the Petrified Forest of Arizona.

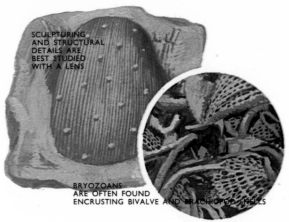

SCULPTURING AND STRUCTURAL DETAILS ARE BEST STUDIED WITH A LENS

BRYOZOANS ARE OFTEN FOUND ENCRUSTING BIVALVE AND BRACHIOPOD SHELLS

Inspection of a fossil with a lens may show delicate details of structure. Some small fossils may be found encrusting larger ones.

Shales may also contain nodules or lumps of limestone. Such nodules are formed by the calcium carbonate in the shale concentrating about a single nucleus. Often the nucleus is a fossil and cracking open a nodule may reveal a perfectly preserved specimen.

Limestones are often fossiliferous – in fact they may sometimes be made up almost entirely of organic remains. Because the rock is so hard, it may be difficult to extract fossils without damage. The best place to look is in the broken fragments which collect at the bottom of exposed cliffs and quarries. These small pieces are easy to inspect and often the processes of weathering clearly expose the fossils. Collecting from unweathered rock is hard work. Large slabs broken off frequently have to be further broken down before fossils are found.

Close examination of fossils, with a hand-lens, may reveal further information. Muscle scars may be preserved on the inside of shells, and growth lines on the outside may reveal the true age of the creature when it died. Comparison with similar present-day forms may suggest something of the conditions of the past, even to the temperature and depth of the sea.

Fossils may have been moved before they were finally buried. Those that have, are often worn and broken, particularly the valves which make the shells of bivalve molluscs. Others are still almost exactly in the same position as when they died. They have been left undisturbed on the sediment that formed the floor of the sea at the time.

Little equipment is needed for collecting fossils. A hammer, a few cold-chisels of varying size, newspaper for wrapping the large fossils, and a number of small pill-boxes for holding smaller specimens. A notebook and pencil are useful for noting exactly the locality the fossils came from, and if possible, the exact layer of rock.

A convenient weight for a hammer is about 2 pound – weighty but not too tiring to carry about. Ordinary coal hammers can be used though the all-purpose geological hammers are better. Apart from a flattened end for breaking off pieces of rock, they have a wedge-shaped end which can be used as a lever, a scraper, a chisel or a trowel.

CHAPTER TWO

The Geological Time Scale

THE GEOLOGICAL TIME SCALE PERIODS AND SYSTEMS AND DERIVATION OF NAMES				DATES IN YEARS B.P. (BEFORE PRESENT)	
PHANEROZOIC EON *(PHANEROS=EVIDENT, AND ZOON=LIFE)*	**CENOZOIC ERA** *(KAINOS=RECENT)*	**QUATERNARY PERIOD** THIS IS A CONVENIENT EXTENSION OF THE TERTIARY PERIOD AND MAY BE INCLUDED IN THE LATTER	RECENT OR HOLOCENE EPOCH *(HOLOS=COMPLETE)*	ABOUT 25,000	
			PLEISTOCENE EPOCH *(PLEISTON=MOST)*	ABOUT 1,000,000	
		TERTIARY PERIOD THE NAME RESULTS FROM AN OLD DIVISION OF STRATA INTO PRIMITIVE SECONDARY AND TERTIARY THE NAMES OF THE SUB-DIVISIONS OF THE TERTIARY AND QUATERNARY PERIODS REFERS TO THE PROPORTION OF MODERN MARINE SHELLS OCCURRING AS FOSSILS IN THE ROCKS OF THAT AGE	PLIOCENE EPOCH *(PLEION=MORE)*	12,000,000	
			MIOCENE EPOCH *(MEION=LESS)*	25,000,000	
			OLIGOCENE EPOCH *(OLIGOS=FEW)*	40,000,000	
			EOCENE EPOCH *(EOS=DAWN)*	60,000,000	
			PALAEOCENE EPOCH *(PALAIOS=ANCIENT)*	70,000,000	
	MESOZOIC ERA *(MESOS=MIDDLE)*	**CRETACEOUS PERIOD**	FROM *CRETA*=CHALK	135,000,000	
		JURASSIC PERIOD	FROM THE *JURA* MOUNTAINS ON THE FRANCO-SWISS BORDER	170,000,000	
		TRIASSIC PERIOD	FROM THE *THREEFOLD* DIVISION IN GERMANY	200,000,000	
	PALAEOZOIC ERA *(PALAIOS=ANCIENT)* — UPPER	**PERMIAN PERIOD**	FROM THE *PERM* AREA OF RUSSIA, WEST OF THE URALS	230,000,000	
		CARBONIFEROUS PERIOD *CARBON-BEARING* (COAL) — DIVISIONS RECOGNISED IN NORTH AMERICA	**PENNSYLVANIAN PERIOD**	255,000,000	
			MISSISSIPPIAN PERIOD	280,000,000	
		DEVONIAN PERIOD	FROM *DEVON* (MARINE SEDIMENTS)	325,000,000	
	LOWER	**SILURIAN PERIOD**	FROM THE *SILURES*, AN ANCIENT TRIBE OF THE WELSH BORDER	360,000,000	
		ORDOVICIAN PERIOD	FROM THE *ORDOVICES*, AN ANCIENT TRIBE OF NORTH WALES	425,000,000	
		CAMBRIAN PERIOD	FROM *CAMBRIA*, THE ROMAN NAME FOR WALES	500,000,000	
CRYPTOZOIC EON		**PROTEROZOIC ERA** *(PROTEROS=EARLIER)* **ARCHAEOZOIC ERA** *(ARCHAEOS=PRIMEVAL)* **EOZOIC ERA** *(EOS=DAWN)* (THE ABOVE ARE FORMAL ERAS)		THE CRYPTOZOIC EON EMBRACES ABOUT 80% OF GEOLOGICAL TIME	SEAWEEDS INVERTEBR

ROCKS are the key to the past. To the geologist they are like the pages of a history book, though far more difficult to read since they may be torn, bent, upside down and scattered over a wide area. The geo-logical time scale, based mainly on the record of sedimentary rocks, covers the span of the Earth's long history and allows geological events to be related in chronological order and assigned to their correct positions in time.

Sedimentary rocks are those formed by the deposition of sediment beneath water. It stands to reason that a certain layer of sediment must be deposited before the layer above it and thus must be older. So it follows that when the rocks are raised above the sea you would expect any rock layer to be younger than the one it is resting upon. This is the *Law of Superposition*. If every region had a simple structure this law would hold true everywhere, but in many areas the layers have been twisted, ruptured and even overturned by earth movements, so that at first glance the reverse of the Law of Superposition may seem to hold true. An even greater complication in drawing up the geological time scale is that no single region contains a complete record of the past. If it did, the thickness of the sedimentary rock covering would be something like one hundred miles. The fact is that deposition of sediment has always been going on in one region while the land is being eroded in another, just as it is today. Take, for example, the case of a region which has just been uplifted from the sea. The simple horizontal layers of sedimentary rock may be folded and squeezed into uplands by earth movements, and these will gradually be worn down by weathering and erosion to (for the sake of convenience) a flat plain. At a much later date, the truncated folds of the ancient uplands may once more be submerged beneath the sea and fresh layers of sedi-

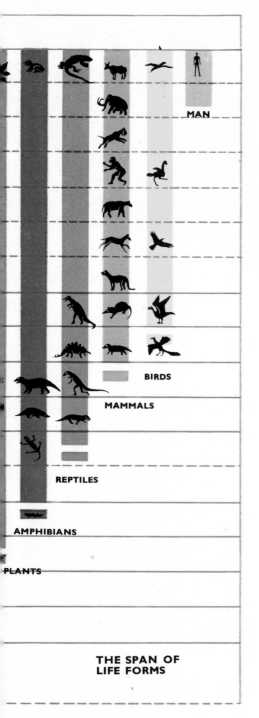

MAN

BIRDS

MAMMALS

REPTILES

AMPHIBIANS

PLANTS

**THE SPAN OF
LIFE FORMS**

Stegosaurus – *a Jurassic dinosaur*

Megatherium – *a giant ground sloth of Pleistocene times*

ment laid down upon them. Then the whole region may later still be uplifted again to form dry land. It will now show a succession of rock layers, but these will *not* represent successive phases in the Earth's history; there may be a gap of many millions of years between the deposition of the older sedimentary rocks and the newer layers above. Fortunately, this time gap can be detected, for the newer, horizontal layers will appear to rest uncomfortably or *uncomformably* upon the older, folded layers beneath. The surface of separation between the two is called an *unconformity*. Unconformities in rock layers always represent a gap in time. Since deposition must have been going on somewhere else in the world during this time gap (when the old uplands were being eroded) there must be rocks somewhere which will fill it. The great problem is how to recognise these in-

14

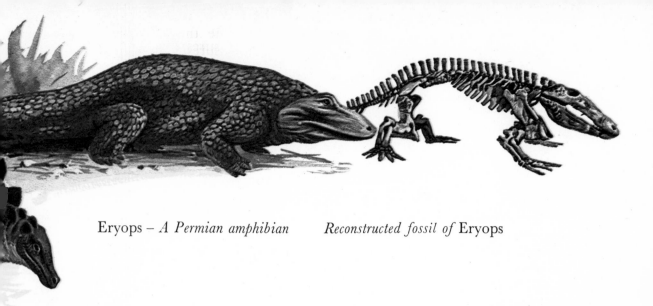

Eryops – *A Permian amphibian*   *Reconstructed fossil of* Eryops

tervening layers where and when they are found. This is where the value of fossils lies.

Fossil Evidence

It was William Smith, the Father of English Geology, who first realised in the late 18th century that certain fossils were confined to certain rock formations. He reasoned, correctly, that it should therefore be possible to identify a particular rock formation, wherever it was exposed, by the fossils it contained. The reason why certain fossils appear only in certain rocks is quite simple: life forms have evolved continuously throughout the Earth's long history. Thus a single species of plant or animal is confined to a certain span of time and its fossilised remains or traces will only appear in rocks laid down during that time. Since the pattern of evolution is clearly recorded in successive rock layers which have not been greatly disturbed it is possible to recognise rocks in one region as filling in a time gap in another region by the fossils of transitional life forms they will contain. And an apparently unnatural sequence of fossils will also show rock layers which have been overturned.

Thus, with the aid of fossils it has been possible to build up a record of the rocks of various ages arranged in chronological order (the geological column) and to draw up the geological time scale.

Volumes, Chapters and Paragraphs

Since the geological history of the Earth covers such a great span of time it is very convenient to divide it up into smaller units (though not all geologists agree that there are natural divisions which have a world-wide application). One dividing line can quickly be drawn at the point in the past where fossils start to appear in considerable numbers in rocks and from then on reveal the changing pattern of life up to the present day. The two sections resulting from this division have been named the Crypto-zoic Eon (Greek *kryptos* = hidden and *zoon* = life) and the Phanerozoic Eon (Greek *phaneros* = evident and *zoon* = life). The Phanerozoic Eon is in turn divided into three *eras* (a division based upon life forms), namely the Palaeozoic Era (Greek *palaios* = ancient), the Mesozoic Era (Greek *mesos* = middle) and the Cenozoic Era (Greek *kainos* = recent). The Crypto-zoic Eon embraces over 80% of geological time, but any attempt to divide it into smaller units can only be done on a local basis owing to the scanty information offered by the rocks where fossils are conspicuous by their absence. Eras of time correspond to *groups* of rocks, but the rocks of the Cryptozoic Eon are collectively termed *Precambrian*.

The eras of the Phanerozoic Eon are further subdivided into *periods* of time, each of which corresponds to a *system* of rocks. Both the period and the system bear the same name, which usually refers to the region where the system was first defined. Thus the Cambrian Period is named after Cambria, the Roman name for Wales, where this system of rocks was first recognised. On the other hand, the Cretaceous Period was so named because of the prominence of chalk amongst the rocks of this system (Latin *creta* = chalk).

Periods of time can be further divided into *epochs* corresponding to *series* of rocks. In general the divisions of a period have a local rather than world-wide importance. For instance, in Britain the Ordovician System is divided into four (or five) series. But the same system in North America is divided into just three series. Series of rock can themselves be divided into *formations*. A coal seam, for example, is a formation.

Calibrating the Time Scale

The geological time scale gives the relative ages of geological events. It indicates that the vast swampy forests, from which the world's great coal deposits are derived, flourished after the Old Red Sandstone of the Devonian Period had been laid down and prior to earth movements which resulted in the uplift of the Appalachians of North America, a range of mountains which probably rivalled the present Alps in height. But it does not indicate the *absolute* age of the Coal Measures, nor the Old Red Sandstone.

It was only the discovery of radioactivity in the closing years of the last century that paved the way for calibrating the geological time scale fairly accurately and thus converting geological or relative time into absolute time. Certain rocks can be dated by the radio-active minerals they contain. For radio-active elements, such as uranium and thorium, gradually break down or *decay* into more stable elements (in these cases lead). Since the rate at which this happens can be calculated, it is possible, by noting the amount of lead produced at the expense of uranium or thorium in such rocks, to determine their age. In practice this is more difficult than it seems, for one gram of uranium will yield just 0·000136 gram of lead in one *million* years. So, a very small error in assessing the uranium/lead ratio means an error of many millions of years in the final calculation of the age of the rock.

Nor is this the only problem, for, generally speaking, radioactive minerals are found in igneous rocks and it is often difficult to date these *geologically*. If the particular igneous rocks happen to occur as a lava flow in sedimentary rock layers then they can easily be dated geologically by the strata immediately above and beneath them. But say they have resulted from the injection of molten material into the sedimentary rocks from below; certainly they are younger than the invaded sedimentary rocks, but how much younger? When the dated igneous rocks can be related closely in age to the associated sedimentary rocks they act as markers in the geological time scale.

CHAPTER THREE

The World as it Was

PALAEOGEOGRAPHY is the study and mapping of ancient lands and seas. The world map as we know it must not be imagined as permanent, for the surface of the world is constantly changing. Through the eons of past time shallow seas have repeatedly invaded the continents and retreated, while great mountain ranges have been uplifted by forces within the Earth and worn down again by the tools of erosion—water, wind and ice. There is even a great deal of evidence to suggest that the continents originally formed one or two great land masses which broke up, the 'pieces' drifting to their present posi-

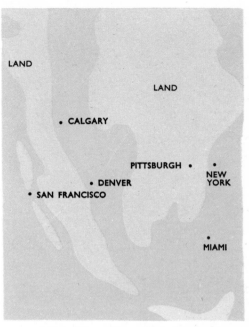

It is doubtful whether many people would recognise the continent pictured in the above map. It is in fact North America as it was some 120,000,000 years ago.

tions. If we were to be presented with a map of North America as it was some 120,000,000 years ago it is doubtful whether we would recognise it as such. But there is no need to go so far back in time to illustrate the changes that have taken place. It was only 8,000 years ago that Great Britain was linked to the continent of Europe by dry land and there is strong evidence in the form of man-made tools to suggest that the Dogger Bank, a large sandbank in the North Sea, was inhabited about 6,000 years ago. Though we shall not be here to see it, the mighty Himalayas, which originally rose out of the sea, will one

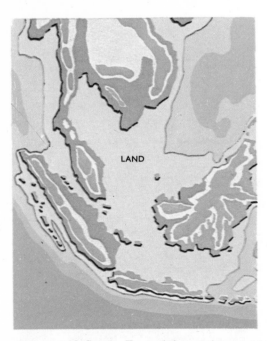

A map of South East Asia as it would appear if the land rose 600 feet (or the sea level fell by a similar amount). It was in fact like this in recent geological time.

A map of the British Isles as they would appear if the sea level rose (or the land sank) 200 feet. Far greater changes have in fact occurred in the past.

world map simply illustrates changes in the relative heights of land and sea.

It is not difficult to find areas which have been submerged in the past, for the tell-tale evidence of sedimentary rocks (rocks laid down beneath water) is hard to destroy completely and, even if these rocks are stripped from the land and carried to the sea, they can still throw a great deal of light on the area from which they were derived. The sedimentary rocks can be identified and related by fossils (traces of animals and plants which have been preserved in various ways, sometimes for many millions of years). Each formation contains its own distinctive set of fossils by which it can be recognised. Thus the extent of Cretaceous rocks at present gives a rough guide as to the extent of land submerged during Cretaceous times. Sometimes the mapping of these rocks produces surprises. The way in which they are graded (according to the coarseness of the material) may suggest that they were derived from a land mass which existed where there is now open sea. It is also possible to trace former land areas which are now submerged. In some cases the courses of ancient rivers can be traced across the sea bed.

Ancient land areas also leave their traces to aid reconstruction. Wind-

day be smoothed away by weathering and erosion, for the greatest mountain ranges are merely temporary wrinkles in the Earth's crust. It is even possible to see minor changes taking place within our own life span as the sea eats away the land in some places and builds on to it by the deposition of sand in others. But it is important to remember that the continents, despite their changes in relief, are permanent features and the changing

A simplified diagram showing how, even after a mountain range has been worn down to a plain, the rocks can give some indication of its former height and the way in which it was uplifted.

The fact that fossils of marine creatures may now be found in rocks high above sea level proves that the relative heights of land and sea have changed considerably throughout the past.

deposited sandstones, continental sediments containing the fossils of terrestrial plants and animals and coal measures bear witness to land having once existed there.

The northern hemisphere at the greatest extent of the Pleistocene ice sheets.

Reconstructing past mountain ranges is not quite so difficult as it may seem, for evidence of their existence remains long after they are no longer visible as geographical features. In the great fold mountain ranges the rock layers have been folded, twisted, overturned and fractured in weird patterns by tremendous pressures. And even after the mountains have been worn down to mere stumps it is possible to tell something of their original size and the way in which they were formed from the truncated folds that remain. Another clue to past mountain ranges lies in the sediment derived from their erosion. This will contain fossils which will date the period of uplift and erosion.

CHAPTER FOUR

Reporting Past Weathers

THE quantity of rain that falls, the direction and velocity of the wind, the atmospheric pressure, the rise and fall of temperatures – such measurements are constantly being made at weather stations all over the world. The readings, which are used for weather forecasting, give a very accurate, day-by-day record of climatic conditions.

But the methodical making of weather charts was only begun in the nineteenth century. What was the weather like 500 or 1,000 years ago? There are no accurate measurements but plenty of general descriptions. Exceptional coldness, wetness or dryness particularly prompted men to put their observations into writing. The clothing known to be worn, the buildings erected and the crops grown also provide information.

But what of the weather before Man appeared? What was the climate like a million years ago? What was it like 500 million years ago? All that survives of these ancient times are the sediments – sands, clays, and limestones – deposited in the seas, lakes and on the land surfaces that then existed. Only from these sediments and the fossil life preserved within them can a picture of the weather be built. This study of past weathers is a branch of geology called *palaeoclimatology*.

Usually only very general information is revealed. Tropical, desert or glacial climates can be recognized but

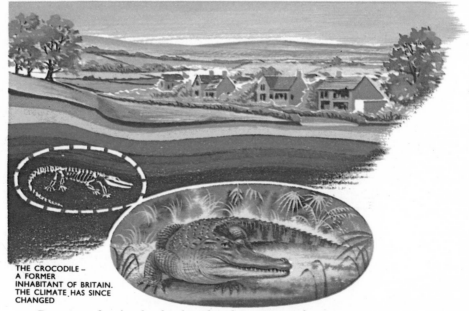

THE CROCODILE –
A FORMER
INHABITANT OF BRITAIN.
THE CLIMATE HAS SINCE
CHANGED

Remains of animals closely related to present day creatures means that, by comparison, a fairly accurate estimation of the past climate can be made. The past creatures presumably lived under similar conditions to their living counterparts.

nothing can be said about the exact rainfall, temperature or atmospheric pressure compared with similar present-day conditions. Sometimes, however, the direction of the wind that blew can be estimated and one recent method estimates the temperature of past sea water to an accuracy of 0·5°C. The temperature of the sea of course has a direct bearing on the surrounding climate.

Hot and Cold Climates

Hot dry desert climates and cold arctic climates are the easiest to identify from surviving sediments. The lack of water in deserts means the sediments will not be carried by rivers but by wind and the effect of wind on small particles of eroded rock is highly characteristic. Particles of a hard resistant mineral, constantly blown about the desert floor as sand develop very spherical shapes and their surfaces are worn quite smooth. The sand propelled by the wind acts as a very effective abrasive. Pebbles and cobbles lying on the ground are polished and faceted on the side facing the prevailing wind. Rock formations protruding from the surface are undercut and sculptured into fantastic shapes.

Rainfall in deserts is a rarity but when it does fall, it falls in torrents. The water rushes down the slopes of high ground carrying all the loose fragments of rock in its path. It spills out into the low plains as a great alluvial fan. The quantity of water soon diminishes by evaporation and seepage leaving a pile of assorted rock fragments behind which may become preserved. Salt deposits (*evaporites*) also indicate desert conditions. The evaporation of water exceeds the rainfall and shallow seas and lakes dry up

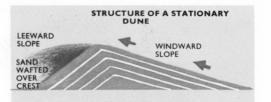

STRUCTURE OF A STATIONARY DUNE

LEEWARD SLOPE

WINDWARD SLOPE

SAND WAFTED OVER CREST

Wind Directions

Sand dunes are built up by the accumulation of layers of sand. A section dug into the side of a sand dune shows each layer distinctly, one piled on top of the other.

During formation the dune is constantly shaped by the wind. It has one steep slope on the leeward side and a gentle gradient on the windward side perhaps of 12 degrees or so. Some of the sand deposited by the wind on the gently sloping surface is swept forward over the crest of the dune and comes to rest at an angle of about 30°.

Dunes are continually moved forward by the prevailing wind. Sand on the gentle windward slope is for ever blown down the steep leeward slope. Consequently the layers in the migrating dune all come to slope at 30°. The sharp (*acute*) angle made by these layers with the dune surface will point in the direction from which the prevailing wind was blowing.

From the study of ancient sand dunes even seasonal changes in wind direction have been detected.

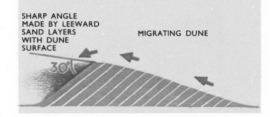

SHARP ANGLE MADE BY LEEWARD SAND LAYERS WITH DUNE SURFACE

MIGRATING DUNE

30°

leaving all their dissolved chemicals behind.

In contrast, prolonged cold conditions produce glaciers, masses of frozen water which move from high to low ground. The glaciers leave their own 'finger-prints' behind. Landscapes are characteristically shaped by the moving ice. Boulders dragged along by

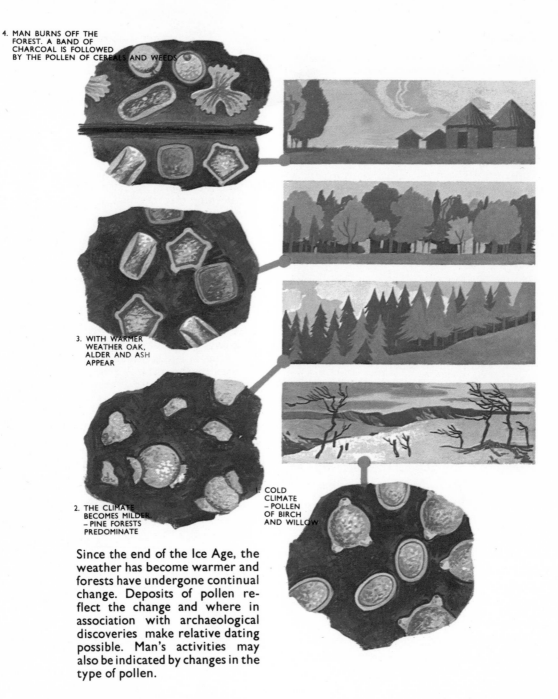

4. MAN BURNS OFF THE FOREST. A BAND OF CHARCOAL IS FOLLOWED BY THE POLLEN OF CEREALS AND WEEDS

3. WITH WARMER WEATHER OAK, ALDER AND ASH APPEAR

2. THE CLIMATE BECOMES MILDER – PINE FORESTS PREDOMINATE

1. COLD CLIMATE – POLLEN OF BIRCH AND WILLOW

Since the end of the Ice Age, the weather has become warmer and forests have undergone continual change. Deposits of pollen reflect the change and where in association with archaeological discoveries make relative dating possible. Man's activities may also be indicated by changes in the type of pollen.

the ice are scarred and grooved where they have been pushed against one another. Particles of rock, chipped-off, are angular with sharp, jagged edges. When the glaciers melt they are left behind as *till*. All sizes, weights and shapes, the particles are very easily identified. Such sediments do not just

belong to the Ice Age of the last million years or so. Glacial deposits preserved in Africa, India and Australia represent an ice advance 300 million years ago. There is evidence that even older ice ages occurred in Pre-cambrian times more than 550 million years ago.

Evidence from Organisms

Nearly all corals are found today in warm tropical and sub-tropical seas. If the temperature of the water falls below 22°C, most corals cannot survive. The occurrence, therefore, of preserved corals and coral reefs in past sediments immediately suggests that the climate at the time was a warm one.

A rough estimation can be made from a number of other fossils which have close relatives living today. Amphibians and reptiles are cold-blooded creatures and flourish in warm moist climates. It is rare to find them in parts of the world which experience extremes of temperatures. Where their remains are plentiful in past rocks, the suggestion is that the climate was warm and moist.

Structures developed by animals may also be significant. The web-footed duck-billed dinosaur known to have lived 100 million years ago almost certainly occupied lagoons and swamps. Only abundant rainfall could have provided such surroundings. The adaptation of fins into limbs and the development of lungs amongst certain fresh-water fishes in Devonian times, 350 million years ago, was probably in response to the shrinking of the inland pools; fishes stranded in the mud could crawl in search of another pool.

Plants can also be used to read climates. Tropical plants are highly characteristic. They nearly all have woody tissues and thin bark. Because there is no seasonal variation, growth rings are not developed. Water plants have air spaces in their tissues and their leaves have breathing pores (*stomata*) only on the upper surface. Plants in dry surroundings have small, leathery or fleshy leaves with few stomata. The evidence from one plant by itself, is not scientifically of great value; but a community of similarly adapted plants is very significant.

Pollen Grains

Our knowledge of the Earth's history during the last million years or so has been greatly expanded by pollen grains, the fertilising powder formed in the anthers of flowers.

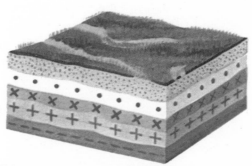

Diagrammatic block diagram of a peat bog to show how successive layers contain pollen of different species in varying proportions (represented by symbols).

Pollen grains vary in size from less than 1/2500 inch in diameter up to 1/100 inch in diameter – visible to the naked eye. They also have a variety of shapes. Some are flat and biscuit-like, others are spherical and covered in tiny spikes, whilst yet others are elaborately patterned. These obvious differences in external appearance allow the plant that produces the pollen grains to be identified. In some cases it is often possible to identify the genus of plant, and sometimes also even the species. The members of certain plant families (e.g. sedges) produce grains so alike that only the family can be identified.

Wind-blown pollen will eventually settle and, if it falls on a peaty region or into water where it will sink to the muddy bottom, it will be trapped. Such situations will preserve the pollen for many years. Boreholes made into lake muds and into peat bogs have produced a series of pollen samples of different ages – obviously, the deeper the borehole into any one bog, the older will be the sample collected. So, by analysing the samples obtained, the changes in the abundance and proportions of the different plant species can be followed, in the case of an old site, over a long period of time. In addition, the species identified may be either warm- or cold-loving and, therefore, the proportions obtained indicate the climate of a particular time.

Pollen analysis has been made use of most fully in Europe, particularly in the western part. For many years forest trees have been the dominant plants of the region. Most of these are wind-pollinated and produce large quantities of pollen. Analysis of pollen samples from various regions have demonstrated quite clearly the effects of the last ice age and how the pattern of vegetation changed as the ice retreated.

The Physicist Discovers a Thermometer

There are three types (isotopes) of oxygen atoms known. Chemically they are identical but their weights differ slightly. The most abundant kind has an atomic weight of 16 (O-16); one of the rarer types has an atomic weight of 18 (O-18).

Oxygen combines with carbon in water to form the carbonate radical, $-CO_3$. The quantity of O-18 incorporated has been found to vary significantly according to the temperature of the water.

Some sea animals may secrete shells of calcium carbonate. They absorb the carbonate radical from the surrounding waters. The abundance of O-18 present in the shell in comparison with the quantity of the normal O-16 will indicate the temperature of the surrounding seas.

By accurate measurement of proportion of O–18 to O–16 in fossil shells, the temperature of past seas can be estimated. So accurate is the method that differences as small as 0·5°C can be detected. Even slight seasonal changes in the temperature of the water can be measured in secretions of the one shell. Of course it is very important that the composition of the original shell has not since been altered by recrystallization.

Shells of belemnites (ancient cephalopods) and foraminifera (protozoans) have been particularly valuable in estimating sea temperature using the oxygen isotope method.

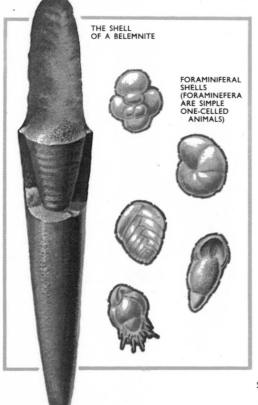

THE SHELL
OF A BELEMNITE

FORAMINIFERAL SHELLS (FORAMINEFERA ARE SIMPLE ONE-CELLED ANIMALS)

The Pageant
of Life

CHAPTER FIVE

The First Signs of Life

A MAGICAL line in the geologic time scale separates the Cambrian period from earlier, Pre-Cambrian times. The first Cambrian deposits – they were formed about 500 million years ago – are rich in fossils, the preserved relics of previous life. Representatives of 14 of the 16 major groups making the animal kingdom are known to have been flourishing; so were most groups of plants. But in the Pre-Cambrian rocks,

graphitic (*carbonaceous*) deposits. These are found scattered in many localities throughout the world and some of them are at least 2,500 million years old. Certainly, in more recent geologic times, carbonaceous deposits are known to have been derived from plant and animal remains. Probably of equally remote age, are certain algal-formed limestones found in South Africa.

Estimated at about 2,000 million

Traces of early Pre-Cambrian life include algal secretions, worm trails, sponge spicules and the possible mould of a brachiopod.

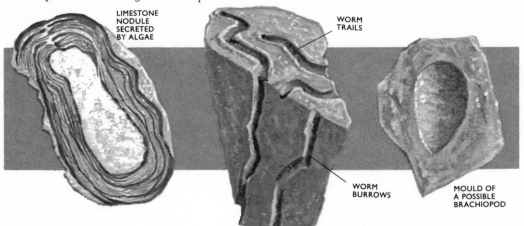

LIMESTONE NODULE SECRETED BY ALGAE

WORM TRAILS

WORM BURROWS

MOULD OF A POSSIBLE BRACHIOPOD

despite their great thicknesses (for Pre-Cambrian times occupy at least four-fifths of the whole geologic time-scale) fossils, as a rule, are exceedingly rare. What are these fossils and why are they so scarce? What light do they throw on the subsequent evolution of life?

Until 1947, intensive searching of Pre-Cambrian rocks in all parts of the world had brought forward meagre evidence of life in these remote times. Probably the oldest signs of life are

years, are certain microscopic fossils found preserved in black flint nodules in Ontario, Canada. The fossils include two types of algae, two types of fungi and a flagellate (i.e. simple protozoan animal). In Montana, U.S.A., the Beltian limestones contain large fossil reefs, some over 20 feet high and 30 feet wide. The reefs are believed to have been formed more than 1,000 million years ago, by certain types of algae. None of the actual algal structures remain however. The Montana limestones have also yielded fossils of sponge spicules and what may be fossil brachiopods.

From the Pre-Cambrian rocks in the Grand Canyon vicinity of the U.S.A. come possible sponge spicules and perhaps the impression of a jelly-fish. In Finland, minute tubes of carbon may be the remains of Pre-Cambrian plants; radiolarian remains come from Brittany in France and in Charnwood Forest, England, and South Africa, 'sea-pens' or soft corals have been discovered. Possible worm tracks impressed in rocks have been found in Pre-Cambrian rocks of all sorts of ages, and the abundant deposits of Pre-Cambrian ironstones may have their origins in the reducing activity of certain bacteria.

In 1947, a late Pre-Cambrian mud flat was discovered in rocks of· the Ediacara hills, South Australia. Pressed into the ancient deposits were the shapes and forms of innumerable soft-bodied creatures. Some are remarkably similar to modern forms. There are many-segmented annelid worms resembling today's ocean-going

Pre-Cambrian Geology

The first Cambrian rocks, with their comparative wealth of fossils, were deposited over 500 million years ago. All older rocks were formed in Pre-Cambrian times. As the world is believed to have been formed 4,500 million years ago, theoretically, Pre-Cambrian times lasted 3,900 million years. But actually the oldest known rocks existing at the Earth's surface are 2,700 million years old, leaving 1,800 million years of the Earth's history unaccounted for.

Pre-Cambrian rocks occur in every continent. Often they are deeply buried but in many areas, uplift and erosion has exposed them at the surface. In fact, in Canada and in Australia they occupy most of the surface. As a rule Pre-Cambrian rocks are hard. If they were not initially igneous in origin (cooled from a molten mass), they were hardened and altered by heat and great pressures (metamorphosed rock).

So far, two very broad divisions of Pre-Cambrian rocks are recognised. The *Archaeozoic* (dawn of life) consists of rocks much older than 2,000 million years and includes deposits with possible traces of life. The *Proterozoic* (first life) incorporates all later Pre-Cambrian rocks.

PRESENT-DAY
SOFT CORALS
THE 'SEA-PENS'

Present-day 'sea-pens' or soft corals. Forms like this have been found in Pre-Cambrian rocks in England, South Africa and Australia.

forms, numerous jelly-fish and more 'soft' corals – the sea-pens. There are undoubted worm trails preserved and several types of animal unknown both today and elsewhere in the fossil record.

The Appearance of Skeletons

The treasure-house of Pre-Cambrian fossils in Australia, together with the meagre evidence from elsewhere, has done much to illuminate what really happened at start of the Cambrian times. The old idea that the groups of animals found in Cambrian times did not exist any earlier is obviously wrong. Certainly they were flourishing in late Pre-Cambrian

27

times, if not before.

Another idea – that the animals did exist in much the same form but have just not been preserved – is not convincing either. Quite a variety of Pre-Cambrian rocks are known which could have preserved hard parts of organisms.

Far more likely is the theory that Pre-Cambrian organisms were all soft-bodied. Very exceptional conditions, as in the Ediacara Hills, would be needed for any chance of preservation. If, too, many of the organisms swam or floated in deep water, there would be even less chance of preservation, for deep-water sediments into which their remains would fall, are rare in geologic record.

The enormous increase in number and types of organisms in Cambrian times would then seem to coincide with the relatively rapid evolution of hard parts in many stocks. As material for building skeletons, e.g. calcium carbonate, seems to have been abund-

ant in Pre-Cambrian seas, the emergence of shells etc. most likely represents an advance in biochemical evolution. The time needed is not as short as the 'sudden' appearance of hard parts in the fossil record would indicate. 'Sudden', in geologic terms, usually represents several millions of years.

The forming of hard skeletons giving support and protection would enable animals to adopt a variety of new modes of life. With more habitats to fill, competition for survival would be lowered. The high rate of evolution that followed in the 20 million years or so of early Cambrian times would then be expected.

As yet, knowledge of Pre-Cambrian geology is far from complete. So often, outcropping in remote areas, great stretches of Pre-Cambrian rock have been left hardly touched. In the past, too, the unrewarding nature of these most ancient of rocks did not encourage investigators. Today the situation is steadily becoming rectified.

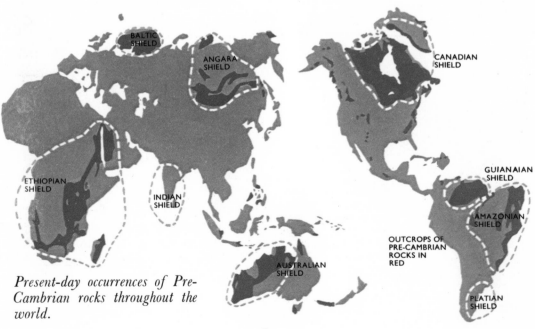

Present-day occurrences of Pre-Cambrian rocks throughout the world.

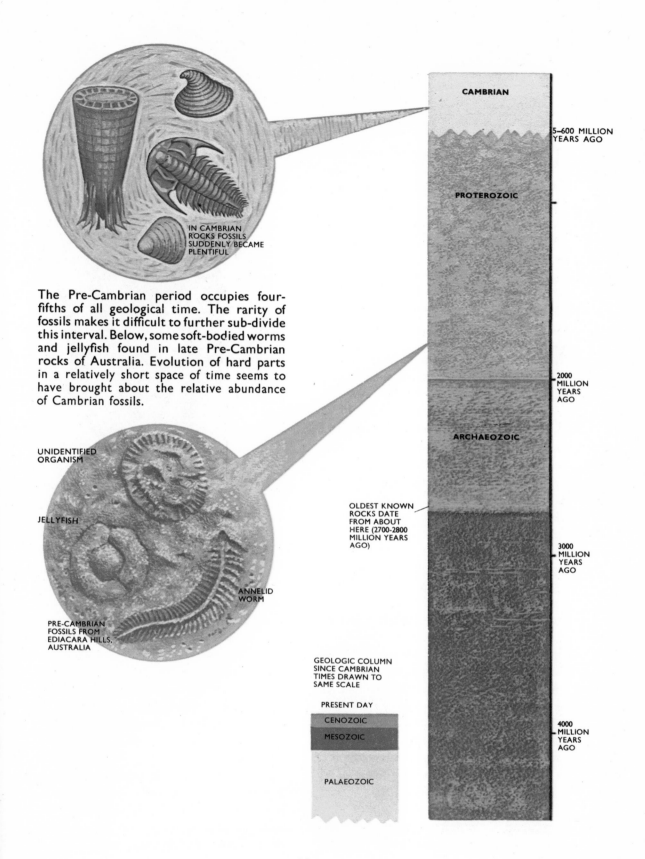

IN CAMBRIAN ROCKS FOSSILS SUDDENLY BECAME PLENTIFUL

The Pre-Cambrian period occupies four-fifths of all geological time. The rarity of fossils makes it difficult to further sub-divide this interval. Below, some soft-bodied worms and jellyfish found in late Pre-Cambrian rocks of Australia. Evolution of hard parts in a relatively short space of time seems to have brought about the relative abundance of Cambrian fossils.

UNIDENTIFIED ORGANISM

JELLYFISH

ANNELID WORM

PRE-CAMBRIAN FOSSILS FROM EDIACARA HILLS, AUSTRALIA

GEOLOGIC COLUMN SINCE CAMBRIAN TIMES DRAWN TO SAME SCALE

PRESENT DAY

CENOZOIC

MESOZOIC

PALAEOZOIC

CAMBRIAN

5–600 MILLION YEARS AGO

PROTEROZOIC

2000 MILLION YEARS AGO

ARCHAEOZOIC

OLDEST KNOWN ROCKS DATE FROM ABOUT HERE (2700-2800 MILLION YEARS AGO)

3000 MILLION YEARS AGO

4000 MILLION YEARS AGO

CHAPTER SIX

Trilobites

THESE extinct animals were the dominant creatures of the Cambrian seas about 500 million years ago. From the early species, many others evolved and reached a peak in the Ordovician Period. They were still important in Silurian times but only a few species survived after then. The latest trilobites lived during the Permian Period, about 220 million years ago, after which they disappeared for ever.

The trilobites form a distinct class of the jointed-limbed animals (the *Arthropoda*). The name of the class is *Trilobita*, after the way in which the body appears divided into three lobes by two grooves running along its length. Like the other arthropods, trilobites had an external skeleton. It was probably horny, and, at least on the upper surface, heavily impregnated with calcium carbonate.

Trilobite fossils are often found only as fragments but a complete specimen will show that as well as the three longitudinal divisions, the body had three divisions in the other direction. At the front end is the semicircular or triangular *head-shield*. The central part of the head-shield is raised and is known as the *glabella*. It is continuous with the axis of the rest of the body. Running across the glabella there are usually a number of grooves or furrows that indicate a segmented origin for the head. The furrows are usually prominent in the earlier trilobites but gradually disappeared as the later ones evolved. Some of the most advanced species

Calymene, *a common type of trilobite, fossilised in a piece of limestone.*

have no furrows at all. The outer parts of the head-shield are known as *cheeks* and in most species they bear the eyes. Each cheek (if eyes are present) is traversed by a fine groove called the *facial suture*. The head-shield frequently has a broad, flat border around it, that curves underneath the head. The glabella may or may not reach to the front of the head-shield. The hind-angles of the shield are often prolonged into spines.

Behind the head is the *thorax* which is made up of a number of segments. In general, the early species had more thoracic segments than the later ones but *Agnostus* and similar

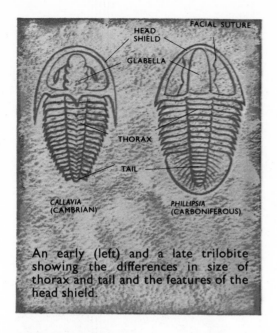

An early (left) and a late trilobite showing the differences in size of thorax and tail and the features of the head shield.

The third body division is the *pygidium* or tail. It is not present in some of the primitive species but in some Ordovician species (e.g. *Asaphus*) it is very large. The pygidium is made up of segments rather like the thorax but the segments of the tail are all fused together and not moveable. It is still divided into axis and pleurae but the axis may not reach to the end.

The majority of fossil trilobites do not give any indication of limbs' but from some rocks, geologists have obtained trilobites showing the under-surface and its limbs. Careful sectioning of rolled-up trilobites has also shown the limb structure. Every segment except the last had a pair of limbs. The first pair of limbs or appendages were long filaments or antennae. The others were all forked – one part being fringed with bristles – and were no doubt used for moving about. The bases of the head-limbs were toothed and presumably acted as jaws. The flattened shape of the trilobites and the position of the

species are obvious exceptions. The central parts of the segments form the *axis* while the lateral parts are called *pleurae*. In life, the segments were free, enabling the animals in some cases to roll up rather as a woodlouse does.

(*Lower left*) *Fossil of the Cambrian trilobite* Agnostus. (*Lower right*) *An impression of the original animal. Both are greatly enlarged, the actual size being shown by the inset.*

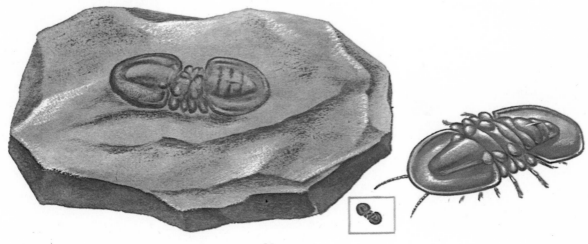

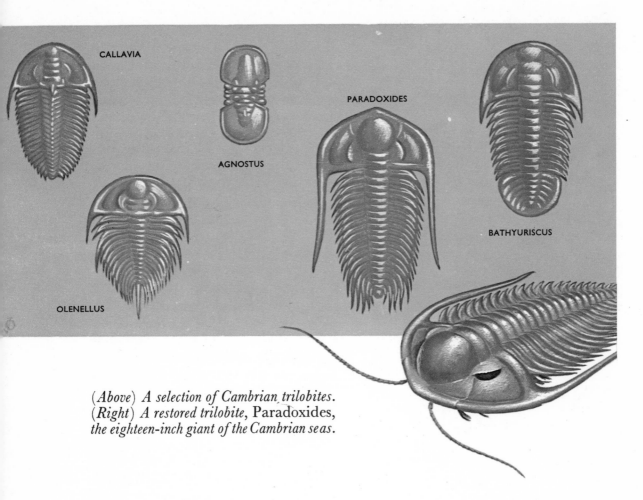

CALLAVIA

AGNOSTUS

PARADOXIDES

BATHYURISCUS

OLENELLUS

(Above) A selection of Cambrian trilobites.
(Right) A restored trilobite, Paradoxides,
the eighteen-inch giant of the Cambrian seas.

eyes on top of the head suggests a bottom-living life on the whole although they could no doubt swim with their many limbs. Some trilobites were the giants of the Cambrian seas, though the largest were only eighteen inches long and the average length was just one inch. Some were so small that they could only have been seen through a microscope.

CHAPTER SEVEN

Brachiopods and Graptolites

BRACHIOPODS (the lamp-shells) are all sea-dwelling animals. Like molluscan shell-fish, their soft parts are protected by a hard shell made up of two valves. But whereas the valves of molluscs are situated about the sides of the animal, in brachiopods they cover the top (*dorsal*) and bottom (*ventral*) surfaces. The ventral valve is normally the larger of the two.

At the rear end of the animal both valves taper to a beak or *umbo*. In one group, the valves are calcareous and hinged along the umbo by teeth. The remainder have horny shells joined by muscles alone. Brachiopods live attached to the sea-floor by a stalk or pedicle. In the hinged group, the stalk cannot pass between the tightly fitting valves and instead leaves through an opening in the umbo of the ventral valve.

The name *Brachiopod*, is derived from the two arms or *brachia* found on either side of the mouth. The arms extend into the surrounding seas and waft water with small plants into the shell. They also provide a large surface area for absorbing oxygen. On numerous occasions paired calcareous structures, sometimes spiral-shaped, have evolved to support the arms. The histories of these developments are well known from study of fossil forms. Brachiopods have lived from earliest Cambrian times. They make up nearly half of the pre-Permian fossil species. From then on they have declined. Five thousand fossil species are known; today there are a mere 150 living forms. However, study of these few surviving animals – their environments and modes of life – has proved valuable in attempting to reconstruct the conditions of the past.

Graptolites

Graptolites are known only from fossilized remains. Thus the structure of their soft parts and their life histories will always remain uncertain. Most of the fossils are mere impressions on shale surfaces; but fortunately a few complete skeletons have been found preserved in limestones and silica nodules.

DIDYMOGRAPTUS NEMAGRAPTUS DICELLOGRAPTUS

Some Ordovician graptolites preserved in slates. The horny skeletons have been completely flattened.

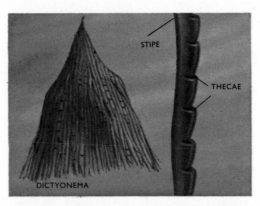

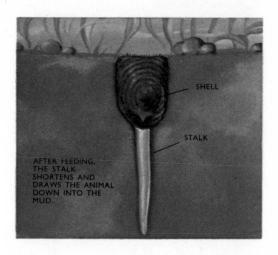

Left. Dictyonema, *a dendroid graptolite. The colony is made up of radiating branches joined by small bars. This was a floating form but some had roots at their tapered end for attachment. Right. A close up of a graptoloid, showing the thecae.*

Lingula – *a surviving brachiopod from Ordovician times. It has always been a specialized mud-dweller.*

Graptolites were colonial animals; numerous individuals lived in cup-like structures (*thecae*) attached to a common thread (*stipe*). The skeleton itself was made up of two layers of chitin. In the earliest graptolites – the *Dendroids* – there were two different types of cup and a thin chitinous thread called the *stolon* ran throughout the colony. The stolon was possibly a similar structure to a noto-cord which would relate the graptolites to the chordate animals – a group which in-

cludes Man. Their colonies were at first large, and branched extensively but later they tended to become simpler.

The other important group, the *Graptoloids*, were without chitinous stolons but are thought to have evolved from Dendroid forms. Further, only one type of cup was present, though the shape of this varied enormously within the group. Branching was not so extensive as in the Dendroids; many forms in fact did not branch at all.

The graptolites made very rapid changes in shape and form as they evolved and are subsequently good fossils for dating the rocks. For instance, sediments formed at one point in time will contain a type of graptolite distinct from those found in sediments deposited shortly afterwards. Moreover most graptolites drifted in open waters. Thus their remains are scattered over a wide area and enable one outcrop of rock to be directly related in age to another, hundreds of miles away. Unfortunately for the fossil record the race became extinct towards the end of the Silurian period.

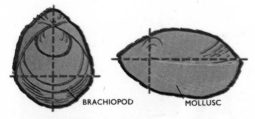

Brachiopods have equilateral shells. A line through the centre divides each valve into two equal halves (left). This character easily distinguishes them from the shells of molluscan bivalves (right).

34

CHAPTER EIGHT

The First Backboned Animals

The first fishes were jawless and fed by digging in the mud. Lampreys and Hag-fishes are the only living jawless fishes.

BACK-BONED animals (*vertebrates*) have been in existence for at least 400 million years. We know this because various bone fragments and fish scales have been found preserved in rocks of this age. ·The age of the rocks has been determined approximately by radioactive dating of associated volcanic rocks. The bone fragments must have been buried in the sediments which gradually became converted into rock. Younger rocks in various parts of the world have yielded a wealth of fossilized remains which show the various stages in the evolution of back-boned animals. By studying fossils of various ages we can see how fishes may have given rise to

An early bony fish with ray-fins. This type gave rise to all the modern ray-finned fishes.

amphibians; how these later gave rise to reptiles and how the latter gave rise to both birds and mammals. All this, of course, took many millions of years and, for an immense period of time, the only back-boned animals were various types of fishes.

How the fishes arose from earlier types of animal is not clear. Many groups of invertebrate animals have been suggested as ancestors of the vertebrates but the most likely group is that containing the starfishes. Some

A placoderm fish, one of the earliest jawed ones. There are several pairs of fins. The placoderms gave rise to both cartilaginous and the higher bony fishes.

members of this group have larvae very similar to those of *Balanoglossus* – a worm-like animal known to be related to the vertebrates because it has gill slits and other associated features.

The earliest traces of fishes, about 400 million years old, are found in some Ordovician rocks of America. But it is not until the upper Silurian rocks, formed some sixty million years later, that complete fish fossils are found. These early fishes were not very large, inches long rather than feet.

Rare discoveries such as this fossil fish help to piece together the story of evolution.

Most of them were heavily armoured with bony plates and scales, especially in the head region. The most striking feature of all these early fishes was the complete *absence of jaws*. They probably fed by sucking up mud and filtering it through the gills. Many of them were flattened from top to bottom and were adapted for life on the sea or river bed. The jawless fishes are placed in a separate group (*Agnatha* – meaning 'no jaws') distinct from all other vertebrates (*Gnathostomata* – meaning 'jawed mouths').

Remains of the first known jawed fishes (*placoderms*), are found in late Silurian deposits formed about 330 million years ago. As well as jaws, they had paired fins. These two features were landmarks in vertebrate evolution. The direct ancestors of the jawed fishes are not known, but they probably arose from some sort of jawless fish in which the bones supporting some of the gills developed into jaws. This may seem startling but the illustration shows that, over a period of millions of years, it is not such a remote

possibility. Placoderms, like the jawless fishes were partly covered with bony armour. The teeth suggest that they fed on other animals. Most of them were small (under a foot long) but there were a few giant species such as *Dinichthys* which reached a length of thirty feet. The placoderms declined at the end of the Devonian Period and later disappeared.

The Devonian Period, which began about 325 million years ago is often called the 'Age of Fishes'. Many jawless fishes existed and all the major fish groups appeared. The shark-like fishes with cartilage skeletons first appeared during this period. They were very like modern sharks, with powerful jaws and stream-lining. They lacked the heavy armour of their an-

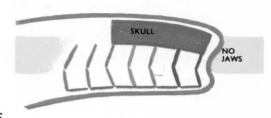

36

An early lobe-finned fish. Fishes of this type gave rise to the modern lung fish and to the land vertebrates.

This early amphibian is not far removed from fishes. Modern amphibians and the reptiles both arose from this sort of ancestor.

cestors and were more mobile. Their hard teeth and spines are commonly preserved in the rocks. All the present-day species live in the sea but some early ones may have lived in fresh water. Many shark-like species became extinct at the end of the Palaeozoic Era but the modern species form a very successful group.

Bony fishes also arose during the Devonian Period. There were, from the beginning, two groups: the ray-finned fish, which include almost all living species, and the lobe-finned fish. The latter are represented today by three lung-fish and that very remarkable fish – the coelacanth. Coelacanth fishes were believed to have been extinct for millions of years but in 1938 one was caught in the Indian Ocean off Africa. Several others have since been caught.

The early bony fishes were quite well armoured and were rather clumsy. The African Bichir is a living

representative of these early types. Most of them, however, were replaced by modern fishes in which the heavy armour is replaced by thin scales. The Bichir, like the early bony fishes, possesses air-sacs opening from the back of the throat. Most modern bony fishes have an air-bladder above the gut. It does not open into the throat and is concerned with the hydrostatic balance of the fish. There are, however, living and fossil fishes that show intermediate stages and it seems that the air-sacs evolved into air-bladders in the ray-finned fishes.

The lobe-finned fishes were very common during the Devonian Period. A most important feature was the internal opening of the nostrils. This meant that they could breathe air. They could probably also move about on their lobed fins. It is certain that, somewhere in this group of fishes, lies the ancestor of the amphibians and all the land vertebrates.

The jaws of vertebrates are believed to have arisen from the bones that supported the third pair of gills in the earlier jawless fishes.

CHAPTER NINE

Vertebrates Conquer the Land

EARTH movements and mountain-building at the end of the Silurian Period resulted in the lifting up of large areas of sea-bed, especially in the Northern Hemisphere. The new land was traversed by rivers and streams and dotted with lakes and swamps. This was the Devonian Period. As yet, the land surface was quite bare; only a few plants were to be found there. Life was centred in the waters of the rivers and lakes where numerous fishes swam. Some of these fishes were heavily armoured and had no jaws. They fed by sucking up mud from the bottom and extracting food. Other fishes did have jaws; they were less heavily armoured and swam freely in the waters. There were two main groups of jawed fishes – those with ray-fins and those with fleshy-lobed fins.

The climate was mainly warm and dry: rivers and lakes periodically dried up. Many fishes were stranded or died through lack of oxygen in their shrinking lakes. But the fishes with lobed fins survived because they could gulp air into their air-sacs, which acted as lungs. They could also move about on their fins and perhaps found plenty of food in the form of dead and dying fish. Some of these animals actually left their drying pools and wandered over the land in search of new stretches of water. Many of them died, but those that survived the longest perhaps found water and continued to live and produce young. These young grew up and sometimes experienced drought. Their drought-resisting ability saved them and the race continued to exist. Very slowly the ability to survive and move on

LOBE-FIN IS ABLE TO LIVE OUT OF WATER

EARLY RAY-FINNED FISHES

RAY-FINNED FISHES
CANNOT SURVIVE IN DRYING POOLS

land improved: the fins gradually became modified into legs. The new animals were the first *amphibians*. They could live on land but were at home in the water and had to return there to breed.

The above is a widely accepted theory of the origin of amphibians – the first land vertebrates – but where is the evidence?

Many of the Devonian rocks are red in colour. Present-day hot, dry regions frequently contain red sands and it is fair to assume that Devonian rocks were formed under mainly dry conditions. The presence of salt deposits also indicates evaporation of water (i.e. drying of lakes, etc.). These deposits contain numerous fossils which show that the ray-finned and lobe-finned fishes were common.

Careful examination of some fossils shows that the lobe-finned fishes possessed air-sacs opening into the throat. In this respect they resemble the modern lungfishes which also live in regions subject to seasonal drought. The lung-fishes gulp air and can survive for a while out of water. The Australian lungfish can use its fins to crawl about on the mud. It is reasonable to expect that the ancient lobe-finned fishes behaved in this way. This sort of evidence strongly supports the theory of the origin of amphibians.

More evidence in favour of the evolution from lobe-fin fishes comes from the Upper Devonian rocks of Greenland. Here, there are some remarkable fossils, believed to be about 300 million years old. The bones of the skull and of the spinal column show striking resemblances to those of the lobe-finned fishes. The presence of five-fingered limbs and strong limb girdles, however, are definite amphibian features. These animals (e.g. *Ichthyostega*) certainly merited the term 'missing link', although they are not thought to be the actual ancestors of modern

ICHTHYOSTEGA ——
AN EARLY AMPHIBIAN
RESEMBLING CLOSELY THE
LOBE-FINNED FISHES.

In open waters, the ray-finned fishes were able to compete successfully but when the waters became shallow and crowded, the lobe-finned fish were at an advantage. They could breathe air and when the water dried up they could probably survive. This type of animal evolved into the primitive amphibians as above.

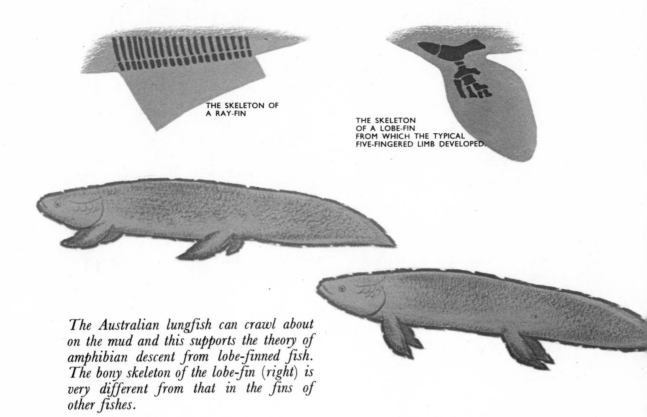

THE SKELETON OF
A RAY-FIN

THE SKELETON
OF A LOBE-FIN
FROM WHICH THE TYPICAL
FIVE-FINGERED LIMB DEVELOPED.

The Australian lungfish can crawl about on the mud and this supports the theory of amphibian descent from lobe-finned fish. The bony skeleton of the lobe-fin (right) is very different from that in the fins of other fishes.

animals. There is then, a wealth of evidence showing how the amphibians probably arose.

Remains in the Devonian and Carboniferous rocks indicate that, for many millions of years, the amphibians remained fish-like although the limbs were developing into the typical five-fingered form. Gradually, the more terrestrial types evolved. The skeleton and, probably, other features became more suited for life on land. The amphibians, however, never came to dominate the Earth in the way the reptiles did later. The amphibians were tied by the fact that they could never completely escape from the water. Even the present-day frogs and toads have, with few exceptions, to return to water to breed. The young stages (tadpoles) live in water and breathe with gills in much the same

way as fishes.

The living amphibians make up only a small fraction of the modern animal world but they are far from being 'surviving relics'. They are highly specialised animals, well adapted for the lives they lead. A modern frog is different indeed from its primitive Devonian ancestor.

At some point way back in time, a group of amphibians developed a more waterproof covering and began to lay eggs that could survive on land. These animals were the ancestors of the *reptiles* which came to dominate the Earth during the *Mesozoic Era* (Middle Life Age, between one and two hundred million years ago). Other groups of early amphibians gave rise to the ancestors of modern forms, while a great many of them died out at the end of the Palaeozoic Era.

CHAPTER TEN

The Ruling Reptiles

THE last dinosaurs or 'terrible lizards' vanished from the Earth more than seventy million years ago. But, for about 100 million years they had dominated the world. There were huge plant-eating forms and fierce carnivores – *Tyrannosaurus* had dagger-like teeth more than six inches long! Together with the flying reptiles and a number of others in the seas, the dinosaurs certainly merited their title 'ruling reptiles'.

Reptiles are cold-blooded animals that originated from amphibians way back in coal-measure times about 250

Seymouria – one of the primitive reptiles with many amphibian characteristics.

million years ago. The reptile embryo (like that of birds and mammals) is enclosed in a sac of liquid (the *amnion*) and this means that the eggs can be laid on land. The reptiles' bodies became adapted for their life on land. The scaly skin developed and the skeleton changed to some extent. Various fossils have been found showing features of both reptiles and amphibians and it is from these fossils that palaeontologists have worked out how the reptiles arose.

The early reptiles were generally small – a foot or two long – and were flesh-eaters. On the land they evolved rapidly and during Permo-Triassic times (200 million years ago) many species appeared. Some became plant-eaters and some even returned to the

An early archosaur about 4 feet long.

sea to give rise later to the ichthyosaurs and plesiosaurs. One line evolved into the turtles of today which still retain some primitive features. Snakes and lizards appeared much later as the descendants of yet another line of

An advanced mammal-like reptile of a type that later gave rise to the mammals.

reptiles. The tuatara of New Zealand is the only living representative of its group and is truly a 'living fossil'.

Mammals developed from one or more reptilian groups that were present during Triassic times. Many of the mammal-like reptiles were clumsy animals several feet long but others were very small. It was a long time before their mammalian descendants became important. The Mesozoic Era belonged to the reptiles – especially to the *Archosaurs* or ruling reptiles.

In late Permian times a group of reptiles took to walking on their hind legs which became longer than the front legs. These animals were the first archosaurs and their descendants dominated the next hundred million years. The crocodile group are the only living archosaurs and they, of course, have given up the habit of walking on

the back legs and have gone back to the water. Birds, too, are descended from archosaur ancestors. The flying reptiles – *Pterodactyls* and others – were also archosaurs but not closely related to the ancestors of the birds.

The word 'dinosaur' usually conjures up visions of large lumbering creatures but, in fact, very many were small. Two distinct groups are bracketed together as dinosaurs because the name was coined before it became ·clear that they were not all closely related. The pelvis differs in the two groups.

Saurischia

The early dinosaurs of this group were all flesh-eaters and walked on their back legs. Plant-eaters appeared later, frequently reverting to walking on all fours. Towards the end of the

The Cretaceous scene here is dominated by the huge flesh-eating Tyrannosaurus, *about 15 feet high. Large bipedal dinosaurs like this balanced their bodies with huge tails. The front legs were often absurdly small.* Tyrannosaurus *fed on the plant-eating Ornithischian dinosaurs like the horned* Triceratops *and the duck-billed* Trachodon. *Flying pterosaurs dominated the air for there were, as yet, few birds.*

PTEROSAUR

TRACHODON

TRICERATOPS

Triassic some very large species appeared. These culminated in the huge *Brontosaurus* and *Diplodocus* of the Jurassic and the terrible *Tyrannosaurus* of the Cretaceous Period.

Ornithischia

These dinosaurs were all plant-eaters. They appeared later than the Saurischians and never reached such enormous proportions. There were both two- and four-footed species but, as in all dinosaurs, the hind legs remained the longest. Many were heavily armoured (e.g. *Stegosaurus* and *Triceratops*). One of the best-known is the Cretaceous *Iguanodon*.

The Decline of the Reptiles

When the reptiles first appeared they had no competitors – other than themselves – and were able to spread and evolve rapidly. For more than 100 million years they dominated the land, sea and air. Then towards the end of the Cretaceous Period they began to decline and at the end of the period (about 70 million years ago) the ruling reptiles disappeared altogether. All that were left were the relatively small groups that survive today. Perhaps the cold-blooded reptiles could not withstand the climatic changes at that time or there may have been some other factor. It has even been suggested that bacteria may have evolved at that time and killed off the dinosaurs. Whatever may have been the reason, they disappeared – leaving the field clear for the birds and mammals.

43

TYRANNOSAURUS

CHAPTER ELEVEN

The Finding of Dinosaur Eggs

IN 1923 a member of the American Museum of Natural History expedition to a red sandstone area of the Gobi Desert in Mongolia stumbled across a complete nest of fossilized dinosaur eggs. These had been laid towards the end of the Cretaceous Period, about 80,000,000 years ago. They lay near the surface partly exposed by millions of years of erosion. On a previous expedition part of an eggshell had been found, but this later chance discovery, hundreds of miles from the nearest inhabitants in a desert area which is more than ten times the size of Great Britain, had surpassed all expectations. Here, at last, was startling proof that at least some dinosaurs laid eggs. Not only that, this particular dinosaur, *Protoceratops*, laid its eggs (fifteen or more of them) in a nest in much the same way that turtles and many birds lay their eggs today.

The brick-red rocks in which the eggs were found consist of fine red grains of sand. They are soft and crumbly and undoubtedly were formed from sand blown by the wind. Mongolia must have been a very dry, hot desert when *Protoceratops* was alive, with sand-storms such as there are in deserts today. Probably the eggs were covered too deeply by the drifting sand for the heat of the sun's rays to hatch them. They became embedded more and more deeply until, by the continuous pressure of the great weight of sand above them, the sand around them became compressed to rock. Meanwhile, the eggs themselves had

been replaced by sand and so were fossilized. Conditions in Mongolia were ideal for forming fossils and it is an ideal place to look for them. There would have been very little water, and air undoubtedly was kept from the animal remains by the drifting sand, so that decay would have been prevented.

Protoceratops lived then in desert conditions. There were probably a few streams or ponds, since turtle

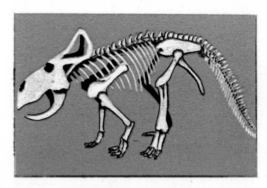

(*above*) *The skeleton of* Protoceratops.

fossils have been found in the neighbourhood, and the tail skeleton of *Protoceratops* suggests that it spent part of its time in the water. Its horny beak and the few teeth it had suggest that it was a plant-eater, perhaps plucking the leaves and branches off the desert shrubs. Besides leaving the water to eat, it also laid its eggs in pits which it dug in the sand dunes. The eggs were laid in circles with the large ends pointing into the middle of the nest. Each egg had a hard shell.

The bones found near the nest were carefully pieced together. Complete skeletons were made of both adults and young. *Protoceratops* was only about six feet long when fully grown. It was the forerunner of the great horned dinosaurs. On the back of its head was a large bony frill to which the jaw and head muscles were attached. It also protected the otherwise vulnerable neck.

The remarkable discovery of part of the skeleton of an ostrich-like dinosaur, *Oviraptor* (or 'egg-stealer'), on a nest of *Protoceratops* eggs suggests that this creature was actually in the act of stealing the eggs.

Ammonites and their Relatives

AMMON was an ancient, ram-headed Egyptian God. Because of a strong resemblance to his rams' horns, certain coiled up shells recovered as fossils from rocks of the past, were called *ammonites.*

Ammonites were *cephalopods* – a group of sea-dwelling molluscs which includes present-day squids and cuttle-fish. Whereas these modern forms have internal shells, ammonites had their shells outside their bodies – just as snails do.

The last species of ammonite became extinct 60 million years ago. Only their hard, fossilized shells are known to us. Fortunately, however, a very

contact with the outside shell-wall, lines of contact or *sutures* are developed. Sutures have been well preserved in fossil shells.

Each chamber represented a stage in the growth of the animal. As the size of the animal increased, it moved forward, secreting a new section of shell. The older chambers were periodically sealed off. Subsequently, they became filled with air and acted as buoyancy tanks, helping to keep the animal afloat. The last chamber of all opened to the outside and here the

In ammonite and nautiloid shells, a strand of tissue – the siphon *– stretched back to the first chamber. It secreted air for*

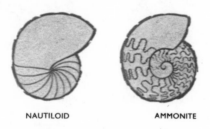

NAUTILOID   AMMONITE

Nautiloids have simple sutures. In ammonites the sutures are more complicated.

close relative, with a similar outside shell, is still living – the pearly-shelled *Nautilus*. The very ancient group to which *Nautilus* belongs (the *Nautiloids*) is believed to have originally given rise to the ammonites. Study of this sole survivor gives some idea of the character and mode of life of both extinct ammonites and nautiloids.

The external shells, unlike snail-shells, are divided up into a number of chambers separated by partitions (*septa*). Where the partitions come in

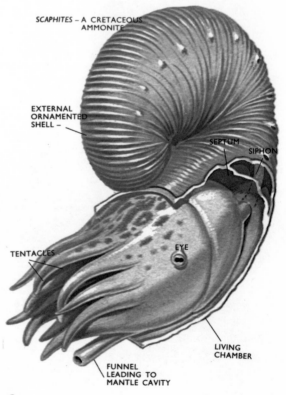

SCAPHITES – A CRETACEOUS AMMONITE

EXTERNAL ORNAMENTED SHELL –

SEPTUM

SIPHON

TENTACLES

EYE

LIVING CHAMBER

FUNNEL LEADING TO MANTLE CAVITY

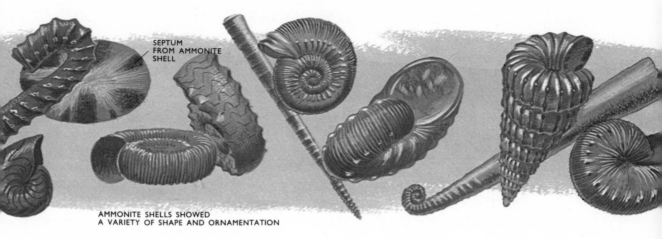

SEPTUM FROM AMMONITE SHELL

AMMONITE SHELLS SHOWED
A VARIETY OF SHAPE AND ORNAMENTATION

adult creature lived.

The head and body of the ammonites and ancient nautiloids probably resembled the head of the surviving *Nautilus*. A large number of tentacles surround a central mouth which is equipped with a tough 'beak'. The very front of the head is made into a thick layer, which covers the opening of the shell when the creature withdraws. Underneath the head is the large mantle cavity containing two sets of gills. When water is squirted out from the cavity through a narrow funnel the movement thrusts the animal forward in the opposite direction. This is how all cephalopods swim.

Nautiloids first appeared in Upper Cambrian times about 450 million years ago. The first shells were not coiled; they were straight tubes. Some of the largest tubes were as much as 15 feet long and 2 feet wide. From the straight shell, a variety of curved, loosely and tightly coiled shells evolved. But by the Triassic Period most of the Nautiloids had declined and only a few coiled forms were left. *Nautilus*, the only survivor, first appeared in Jurassic times, 150 million years ago.

The first ammonites are thought to have evolved from the Nautiloids during the Ordovician Period but they did not increase in number until Devonian times. They appeared very similar to their Nautiloid ancestors, but the *sutures* were complicated and not simple contacts.

Ammonites were at their peak during the Mezozoic era, and their shells show every sort of shape and ornamentation. The largest coiled shells were more than 8 feet in diameter. Their very rapid evolution and wide occurrence makes them as good as the *graptolites* for dating the rocks. Why this seemingly successful group should suddenly die out is one of geology's big mysteries.

Showing the abundance of the three cephalopod groups through geological time and their probable relationship to one another.

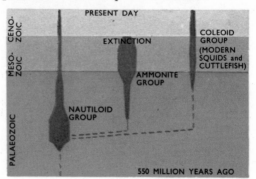

PRESENT DAY

CENO-ZOIC

MESO-ZOIC

PALAEOZOIC

EXTINCTION

COLEOID GROUP (MODERN SQUIDS and CUTTLEFISH)

AMMONITE GROUP

NAUTILOID GROUP

550 MILLION YEARS AGO

47

CHAPTER THIRTEEN

Birds of Ancient Skies

WHEN the sea and the land had been colonized by life, the skies still remained unoccupied. The first creatures to invade the air were insects. Fossils of their wings have been found in Carboniferous rocks, 280 million years old. One hundred million years later the larger, heavier backboned creatures (*vertebrates*) took to flight. First came the *Pterosaurs* – true reptiles related to dinosaurs. Their earliest remains are known from Lower Jurassic rock (180 million years old). They drove themselves through the air or perhaps glided, using a dry flap of skin stretched between a very long finger and the sides of the arms, body and legs. Then the birds appeared.

The birds were related to the Pterosaurs for they had descended from the same group of reptilian ancestors. But they had developed feathers – structures unknown in reptiles and, in fact, any other group of creatures. Feathers insulated birds against the outside climate and enabled them to become warm-blooded. Special feathers fitted to the forearms and tail provided a method of flight.

The first fossil bird known, *Archaeopteryx*, was discovered in Upper Jurassic rock 140 million years old. Almost certainly, birds were flying at an earlier date than this, for *Archaeopteryx* is already quite an advanced type. The absence of more primitive

CLAWS
FOR GRASPING

ARCHAEOPTERYX – THE FIRST
BIRD KNOWN. THE JAWS WERE
ARMED WITH TEETH AND EACH
FOREARM HAD THREE CLAWED FINGERS
FOR GRASPING

Birds probably evolved from a group of reptiles that took to tree-life in Triassic times.

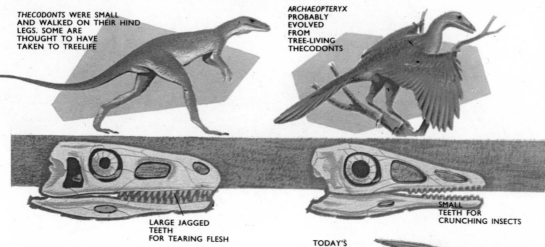

THECODONTS WERE SMALL AND WALKED ON THEIR HIND LEGS. SOME ARE THOUGHT TO HAVE TAKEN TO TREELIFE

ARCHAEOPTERYX PROBABLY EVOLVED FROM TREE-LIVING THECODONTS

LARGE JAGGED TEETH FOR TEARING FLESH

SMALL TEETH FOR CRUNCHING INSECTS

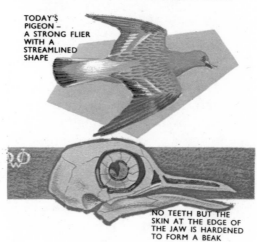

TODAY'S PIGEON – A STRONG FLIER WITH A STREAMLINED SHAPE

NO TEETH BUT THE SKIN AT THE EDGE OF THE JAW IS HARDENED TO FORM A BEAK

birds in the fossil record is most likely due to poor preservation.

Through succeeding Cretaceous times, birds and *pterodactyls* (descendants of the pterosaurs) were flying side by side. In comparison with the flimsy flaps of skin propelling the pterodactyls, the birds' wings were sturdy structures and were not so easily damaged. Pterodactyls, together with many other reptiles, became extinct near the end of the Cretaceous Period (70 million years ago) and quite possibly the increasing competition from the birds contributed to their downfall.

The First Fossil Bird

Early in 1861, workmen quarrying limestone near Solnhofen, Bavaria, discovered the fossilized impression of a bird's feather. Soon after, in a nearby quarry, an almost complete, fossilized bird skeleton was found showing feathers attached to the fore-limb and to the tail. The importance of the discovery was immediately realized. This ancient bird was a link in the chain between modern birds and the ancestral reptiles. It was called *Archaeo-*

pteryx (Greek, *Archaios*, ancient; *pteryx*, a wing).

Archaeopteryx was in many ways very unbirdlike. For instance the elongated upper and lower jaws were equipped with short cylindrical teeth; in modern birds, teeth are absent and a horny beak has been developed. The reconstructed brain appears reptilian rather than birdlike, the hind limbs were the same length as the fore limbs and the creature possessed a long reptilian tail. Further, every bone in the skeleton was solid – unlike today's birds which have some hollow bones filled with air. But the feathers, which are preserved

49

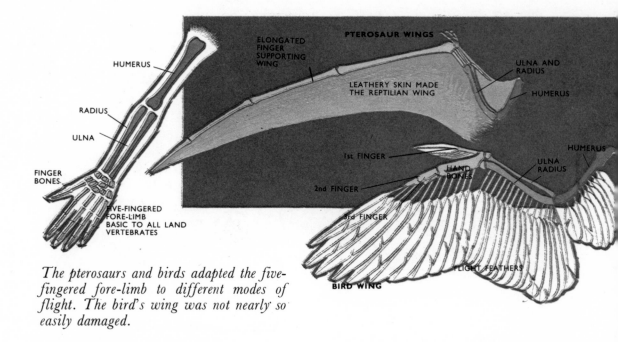

HUMERUS

RADIUS

ULNA

FINGER BONES

FIVE-FINGERED FORE-LIMB BASIC TO ALL LAND VERTEBRATES

ELONGATED FINGER SUPPORTING WING

PTEROSAUR WINGS

LEATHERY SKIN MADE THE REPTILIAN WING

ULNA AND RADIUS

HUMERUS

1st FINGER

2nd FINGER

3rd FINGER

HAND BONES

HUMERUS

ULNA RADIUS

FLIGHT FEATHERS

BIRD WING

The pterosaurs and birds adapted the five-fingered fore-limb to different modes of flight. The bird's wing was not nearly so easily damaged.

in every detail, could have belonged to a modern bird. Large flight feathers were attached to the wings and tail and the body was covered in a layer of smaller feathers.

Archaeopteryx was probably a very feeble flyer. The keel, which is an extended plate on the breast-bone of most modern birds, was very small and could not have supported very large muscles for powering the wings. Also the long rear limbs and cumbersome tail would have prevented strong flight. Probably, *Archaeopteryx* was most at home gliding from branch to branch in the Upper Jurassic forests. Certainly it could perch on boughs, for the first of its four-clawed toes rotated backwards and could be moved in the opposite direction to the other three. This pincer-like device must have been perfect for grasping.

Cretaceous Fossil Birds

Not until well into Upper Cretaceous times, a gap of 55 million years, is the next glimpse of bird life obtained.

This scarcity of fossils is not altogether surprising. If the early birds were largely tree-dwellers, their dead bodies would fall to the ground and be destroyed by other creatures or by natural weathering processes. Only rarely would a bird be swept out to sea, drowned, and preserved in marine sediments.

During the long interval, rapid evolution must have taken place, for Upper Cretaceous birds are far more modern in appearance and there were many different sorts. Most of the relics, as would be expected, are of sea birds and the best preserved of them come from the chalky Cretaceous rocks of Kansas, U.S.A. *Ichthyornis* was a smal-lish bird, 9 inches in height, rather resembling our present-day tern in appearance. There is a strong possibility that its elongated jaws were armed with teeth. Though it was a bird well adapted for swimming on the sea, a strongly developed keel on the breast bone shows that it was also

Birds from Reptiles

The ancestors of the birds are thought to be a group of smallish, Triassic reptiles called *thecodonts*. Perhaps seeking new hunting grounds, some of the thecodonts are believed to have taken to the trees. Their forelimbs would become increasingly strong as adaptions for climbing whilst manoeuvring on narrow branches would develop a good sense of balance. Insects were the chief food supply so small teeth would be more suitable than large teeth.

Finally these creatures would have started to leap through the air, from bough to bough, balancing themselves with their long tails. The appearance of feathers – probably quite accidental – provided the equipment for true gliding and flight.

length. The jaws were extremely long and equipped with numerous small teeth. The webbed feet, though excellent adaptions for diving, were probably useless for walking on the land.

A number of other types of bird have been found in rocks of Upper Cretaceous age in many different parts of the world. From Cambridge in England comes the almost complete skeleton of *Enaliornis* – a pigeon-sized sea-bird; possible ancestors of the flamingoes have been found in Sweden, and in France, a leg bone was discovered of what could be an ancestral goose. In Canada, a single jaw bone is thought to have belonged to a giant land bird, *Caenognathus*, which like *Hesperornis* had given up flight.

In later rocks of Tertiary age the birds were becoming very modern looking indeed. The upper and lower jaws had lost their teeth and a horny beak had developed for feeding. About 500 fossil forms, many of them closely related to present day birds, have been found. Unfortunately most of the remains are very fragmentary.

a strong flier. Another bird, *Hesperornis*, which hunted in the same seas, was 6 foot in height and had become so adapted for life on the water, that it had lost its powers of flight. There is no keel on its breast-bone and its forearms (wings) were each reduced to a single fragile bone a few inches in

ICHTHYORNIS HAD THE APPEARANCE OF TODAY'S TERN

HESPERORNIS – A LARGE, FLIGHTLESS SEA-BIRD

Two cretaceous sea-birds. Hesperornis was 6 feet long, Ichthyornis only 9 inches.

CHAPTER FOURTEEN

The Mammals Take Over

MAMMALS are found almost everywhere on Earth – on land, sea and sky. Man, whales and bats are all members of this large group of warm-blooded animals that dominate the animal world. Yet the mammals are comparative newcomers to the scene. One hundred million years ago the world was 'ruled' by the dinosaurs – huge cold-blooded reptiles with tiny brains. These 'ruling reptiles' gradually declined and, about seventy million years ago, they disappeared, to be replaced by the warm-blooded and more intelligent mammals.

The mammals did not suddenly appear at this time, however; they had been in existence for nearly one hundred million years but had been 'overruled' by the dinosaurs. The mesozoic mammals were mostly small and probably fed on insects. Relatively few fossil mammals are known from the Jurassic and Cretaceous rocks.

The characteristics of mammals are hair, warm-bloodedness and the ability to feed their young on milk. These features are of little use to the palaeontologist but there is another important one. All living mammals have only a single bone (*the dentary*) in the lower jaw. Modern reptiles have more than one, so did the early ones. Mammals evolved from reptiles during

Macraucbenia (*left*) *and* Toxodon, *two of the many peculiar South American herbivores that survived for much of the Tertiary period until the continent was reconnected to North America.*

the Triassic and Jurassic Periods. One of the important changes was the gradual reduction of the smaller bones of the lower jaw. In mammals these are now found as the tiny bones in the ear! We know this because fossils have been found in various rocks which

Two of the archaic hoofed mammals that existed in Eocene times about 60 million years ago. They were replaced early on by more modern types.

show this gradual transformation.

There were many of these mammal-like reptiles in Triassic times. They arose as an offshoot of the primitive reptiles and soon began to show certain characteristics. The limbs, which had been sprawling in the early reptiles, became vertical. The brain case became larger and the smaller jaw-bones diminished further. Some of these animals were quite large and there were both plant-eaters and flesh-eaters. Presumably, as the mammal-like skeleton evolved, other mammalian features appeared hair and warm-bloodedness for example. Most of the mammal-like reptiles disappeared in the Jurassic, leaving only the small shrew-like mammals already mentioned. These changed very little for millions of years.

Monotremes – the egg-laying mammals – were almost certainly living in Jurassic times although no fossils have been found. These animals (e.g. the duck-billed platypus) have hair and feed their young on milk, but they have so many reptilian characteristics that they must have evolved early on.

Marsupial mammals – those that carry their babies in pouches – first

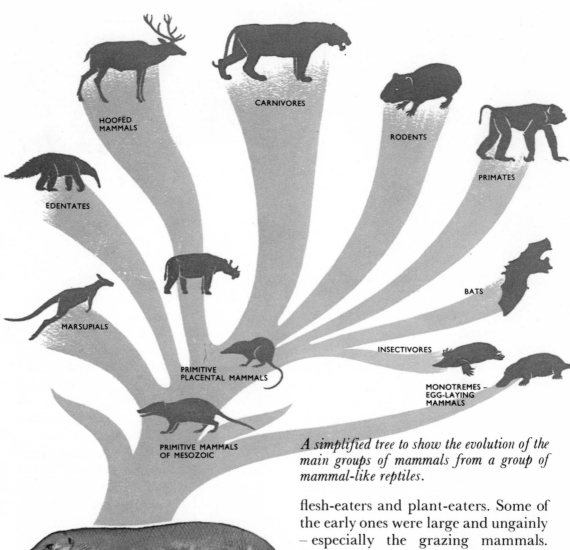

HOOFED MAMMALS

CARNIVORES

RODENTS

PRIMATES

EDENTATES

BATS

MARSUPIALS

INSECTIVORES

PRIMITIVE PLACENTAL MAMMALS

MONOTREMES – EGG-LAYING MAMMALS

PRIMITIVE MAMMALS OF MESOZOIC

A simplified tree to show the evolution of the main groups of mammals from a group of mammal-like reptiles.

appear in upper Cretaceous rocks about one hundred million years old. The true placental mammals probably appeared at about the same time. These were small insect-eating mammals with sharp teeth.

When the dinosaurs disappeared, the mammals were able to colonize many habitats and natural selection produced many different forms. The insect-eating ancestors produced both

flesh-eaters and plant-eaters. Some of the early ones were large and ungainly – especially the grazing mammals. They were not very successful however and died out within a few million years. As well as some of these archaic groups, all the modern mammal groups were in existence by Eocene times (about 60 million years ago). As time passed, the animals became more and more like those of the present day.

The marsupial mammals were not so advanced as the placentals and in most parts of the world they disappeared. However, the Australian continent became separated before placental mammals appeared there – probably in late Cretaceous times. Marsupials were able to spread in the absence of competition and they evolved into many species. The same habitats were available there as elsewhere and, just as the placentals produced carnivores, herbivores, tree-dwellers etc., so have the marsupials. There is even a marsupial mole, very like the placental mole. This sort of similarity is called *parallel evolution*. The only placental mammals that were in Australia before Man arrived there were numerous bats and rats that presumably spread through the chain of islands from Asia.

Marsupials also occur in South America. For a long period of Tertiary time this continent, too, was isolated. The marsupials developed a number of types there but only the opossums survive. When the continent was reconnected to North America, placental types migrated south and replaced most of the marsupials. A number of herbivorous placentals had reached South America before its isolation, however, and produced many strange species. The continent still has some characteristic placental mammals – the armadillo, sloths and ant-eaters – but most of the large grazing animals disappeared when the placental carnivores arrived.

The other regions of the world were dominated by placental mammals in the Tertiary Period. Just as reptiles had

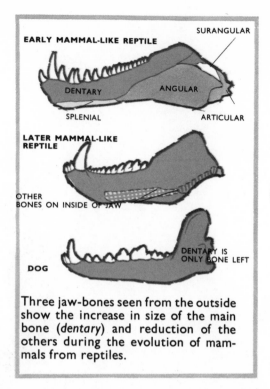

Three jaw-bones seen from the outside show the increase in size of the main bone (*dentary*) and reduction of the others during the evolution of mammals from reptiles.

conquered land, sea and air, so did the mammals.

The bats are truly flying mammals. Whales live entirely in the seas. These mammals all evolved from the primitive insect-eating ones when the reptiles disappeared. They filled the niches left by the reptiles and really did take over the world.

The European Wolf (left) and the Marsupial Wolf showing the similarity developed through parallel evolution.

55

The mammoth was an animal ideally adapted for life on the margins of the ice sheets during the Great Ice Age of Pleistocene times.

CHAPTER FIFTEEN

Fossil Plants – History of the Plant Kingdom

SUNLIGHT 2 000 million years ago was being used by plants just as it is used today – for building simple chemical substances into complex foods. Only traces of these very ancient plants are preserved in the rocks. They were all probably *algae*, very simple water-dwelling plants. Algae, unlike most land plants have no water-proof outer coating (*cuticle*) nor do they develop special tissue (*vascular* tissue) for transporting water and foodstuffs.

About 550 million years ago, the remains of animals suddenly became more numerous in the fossil record. This was the start of the Cambrian period. There are also a few remains of plants. Surprisingly, these remains are not of the simple, water-dwelling algae. Instead there are specialized vascular (woody) tissues and wind-blown spores with outer cuticles. Several groups of land plants seem already to have emerged – mosses and liverworts (*Bryophytes*), spore-bearing plants such as today's ferns, club-mosses and horsetails (*Pteridophytes*), and seed ferns (*Pteridosperms*). Early *Gymnosperms* (seed-bearing plants) may also have been present. How these groups evolved, it is difficult to say. There is no fossil evidence. But certainly plants must have invaded the land long before, in Pre-cambrian times. Perhaps each group evolved from a different group of algae and had solved the problems of living on the land in different ways. There seems no reason why vascular tissues, cuticles, secondary wood, leaves and roots should not evolve more than once independently.

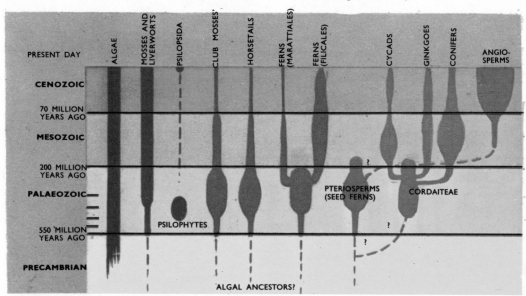

A chart showing the sequence of the main plant groups in geologic time. Because of an incomplete fossil record the evolution from one group to another is uncertain. The origin of the angiosperms is particularly open to question.

Labels on illustration: LEPIDODENDRON, SIGILLARIA, MONKEY PUZZLE TREE, CALAMITES, LYCOPODIUM A PRESENT-DAY CLUB 'MOSS', EQUISETU A PRESE HORSETA

A Carboniferous swamp-forest 250 million years ago. There were no flowering plants but the other main branches of the vegetable kingdom had emerged. The soft-tissued club 'mosses' that survive today are relatives of the ancient scale trees Sigillaria *and* Lepidodendron. *The counterparts of our spindly horsetails were woody and some stood 100 feet high.* Cordaites *was an ancient gymnosperm and seems a particularly close relative of today's Monkey Puzzle tree. Ferns covered the ground; some grew into shrubs or small trees. In structural details, most of them differed from today's ferns. Seed ferns were small but numerous. Perhaps they were the ancestors of the flowering plants.*

Another gap follows, with no more plant remains. Then in Silurian rocks 350 million years old, there are found the *Psilophytes* – simple land plants with vascular tissue but no distinct leaves, roots or stems. Psilophytes were the first land plants discovered and for a long time have been thought the undoubted ancestors of all other land plants. But more highly developed land plants are now known to have been living 200 million years before. It seems likely that Psilophytes are only the survivors of some earlier primitive stock.

But if higher plants were in existence in Silurian times where is the evidence? The only fossil preserved is a leaf of a club moss (a pteridophyte). The discrepancy seems due to the different localities of plants. The Psilophytes inhabited low mud flats near the water; there was always a strong chance that the land would sink and the plants be preserved under the invading water. The more advanced land plants probably lived inland, on higher ground, where surroundings were more varied. The chances that they would become buried with sediment was much less likely. However, in following Devonian times battered logs have been preserved in marine sediment as though

CORDAITES

MODERN FERN

GIANT FERN

carried by rivers into the sea.

The Carboniferous period followed and in coal seams 250 million years old, the first really extensive picture of plant life on land is given. Coal is the fossilized remains of swamp forests of the time. Considerable evolution must have taken place over the millions of years since the Cambrian period. The *Pteridophytes*, *Pteridosperms* and the *Gymnosperms* had become varied.

Amongst the *Pteridophytes* there were relatives of today's horsetails. But these forms were not small and delicate like our present species. They stood up to 100 feet high and had woody trunks. But they possessed some features in common with todays forms – stems with lengthwise ribbing, and points along the stem (*nodes*) bearing whorls of leaves. The club 'mosses' (*lycopods*) were also large and woody.

Amongst the *Gymnosperms*, a group called the *Cordaitales* were the most numerous. They formed large woody trees. The *Cordaitales* became extinct in Permian times but probably gave rise to all later gymnosperms.

The most important group of today's gymnosperms are the conifers. Conifers increased in number towards the end of the Carboniferous period. Today the group is represented by such forms as the Monkey Puzzle tree, the Pine and Larch, the Juniper and Cypress and the Yew. Other groups of gymnosperms living today are the *Cycads* – trees with stout unbranched stems, and a crown of large fern-like leaves. They first became prominent in Jurassic times. Related to the Cycads is the *Ginkgo* or Maiden-hair tree. The group of plants to which it belongs stretch back to late Carboniferous times.

Also amongst the Carboniferous fossils recovered are numerous *Pteridosperms* (Seed-Ferns). They looked like ferns yet bore seeds instead of spores. They survived until Cretaceous times and then became extinct.

Possibly they are the ancestors of the last great group of plants to appear – the angiosperms or flowering plants.

Angiosperms first appear in Middle Cretaceous rocks 120 million years old. They were already quite varied. They include forms very similar to many present-day forms – magnolias, oaks and poplars. They very rapidly became the dominant group of plants. In the face of this vigorous competition many old groups of plants declined.

The sudden emergence of the angiosperms as an already varied and distinct group is probably due to poor preservation in the fossil record. Again it seems likely that early evolution took place on high ground where there was little chance of remains becoming fossilized. Perhaps the angiosperms stretch back as far as Permian times.

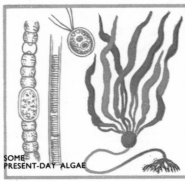

SOME PRESENT-DAY ALGAE

The first plants probably resembled our present-day algae. They lived in the sea and had no vascular tissue or cuticle. Perhaps most of today's group of land plants descended independently from algae. They would have passed through a simple stage resembling the primitive fossilized *Psilophytes*.

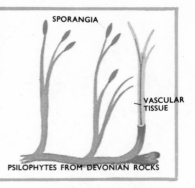

SPORANGIA

VASCULAR TISSUE

PSILOPHYTES FROM DEVONIAN ROCKS

THE SEED WAS ENCLOSED AND SUPPORTED ON A SHORT STALK

LEAF OF SEED FERN

Seed ferns looked like ferns but bore true seeds like gymnosperms and angiosperms. They were abundant in Carboniferous times but died out in the Cretaceous period. Their seeds were enclosed like the angiosperms – not borne naked on cones like the gymnosperms. Perhaps they were the ancestors of the angiosperms.

FLOWERING PLANTS ALSO HAVE ENCLOSED SEEDS

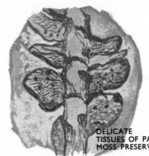

Mosses and liverworts have very delicate tissues which are rarely preserved in the fossil record. They are however very ancient groups, and probably date from Cambrian times.

DELICATE TISSUES OF PAST

MOSS PRESERVED IN CARBONIFEROUS ROCK

PRESENT-DAY MOSS

FUNGI PRESERVED IN THE WOOD OF A CARBONIFEROUS TREE

The fossil remains of fungi are also rare. From the little that is known about their history, there seems to have been hardly any change in their habits or structures at least since Carboniferous times. Different groups of fungi probably evolved from different algal ancestors.

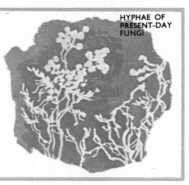

HYPHAE OF PRESENT-DAY FUNGI

The Palaeozoic
World

CHAPTER SIXTEEN

The Cambrian Scene

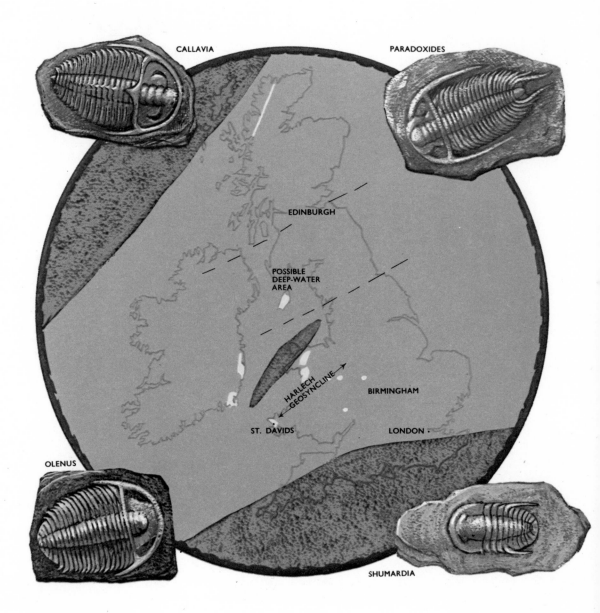

A map showing the possible distribution of land and sea around Britain during Cambrian times. Zone fossils are inset. Present-day outcrops are yellow.

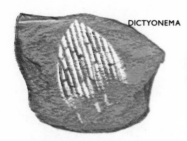

DICTYONEMA

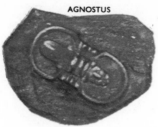

AGNOSTUS

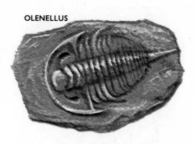

OLENELLUS

WHEN the Palaeozoic Era of the Earth's history dawned some 500 million years ago the land masses were already many, many millions of years old, and already they had undergone vast changes. Great mountain ranges had been uplifted by earth movements and worn down by the tools of erosion, thick ice sheets had scraped their way across the face of the land, and shallow seas had repeatedly encroached upon the continents. But the opening of the Palaeozoic Era is an important date in the history of the Earth, for it is in rocks formed at this time that the record of life clearly makes its appearance. From this date onwards, the unfolding history of the Earth can be followed step by step.

Fossils of almost every invertebrate group have been found in the Cambrian rocks but there were no vertebrates (back-boned animals) or land-living organisms. All the known fossils are of marine origin. The most important fossils are the *trilobites*, some of which are quite common. Trilobites existed throughout the Palaeozoic Era and then became extinct. They were related to the crabs and lobsters, and, like them, had horny external skeletons. Trilobite fossils are easily recognised by the head shield, segmented thorax and tail (*pygidium*) although frequently one or more of these parts are missing. The zoning of the Cambrian rocks is based upon the

succession of trilobite species. Many zones are named after the dominant trilobite, but it is sufficient now to be able to recognise Lower, Middle and Upper Cambrian rocks by their fossils.

Lower Cambrian rocks contain a group of fossils typified by *Callavia* and *Olenellus*. The head-shield normally has a complete margin not crossed by grooves (*sutures*) from the region of the eyes. The tail, when present, does not have lateral lobes. Many other trilobites are present (e.g. *Agnostus* and *Microdiscus*) but these are not of value in dating the rock for they occur in the later rocks too.

Middle Cambrian rocks are typified by fossils of the genus *Paradoxides* which includes the largest of all trilobites. *Paradoxides* differs from Lower Cambrian fossils in having perfect facial grooves and a true tail (*pygidium*). The central part (*glabella*) of the head-shield is wider at the front than in *Callavia*.

Olenus is the typical fossil genus of the Upper Cambrian. The glabella does not reach to the border of the head-shield and the tail is well formed, with lateral lobes. This and closely related genera are used to zone the Upper Cambrian rocks. A common fossil in this group of rocks is the brachiopod *Lingulella davisi*.

Cambrian Britain

At the top of the Cambrian succession in Britain is a series of rocks called the *Tremadoc*. They are mainly

An impression of marine life in the Cambrian. Trilobites, jellyfish and sponges dominate the scene.

slates and shales and contain the trilobite *Shumardia*. This resembles the Ordovician species more closely than the other Cambrian ones. Furthermore, the first graptolites (*Dictyonema* species) make their appearance. The Tremadoc was once included in the Ordovician but, because there is a definite physical break (*unconformity*) above it, the Tremadoc series is now regarded as the top of the Cambrian.

Although trilobites are the most important Cambrian fossils, *brachiopods* are also of some value. They are bivalve animals whose shells resemble those of molluscs but internally they are very different. Some brachiopods are found in the seas at the present time. Snail-like and squid-like molluscs also became important during the later part of the Cambrian.

Cambrian rocks appear at the surface in only a few areas in Wales and the Midlands and in the north-west of Scotland. Boreholes in Buckinghamshire, however, pass through Cambrian rock, so it is likely that most of the British area was under the Cambrian sea. Whenever the base of the Cambrian is seen, it rests on a very irregular surface of pre-Cambrian rock, indicating a long period of erosion. Thus, the area must have stood above sea-level in late pre-Cambrian times. Remnants of this ancient land surface can be seen in the north-west of Scotland and the Outer Hebrides.

At the beginning of the Cambrian period, the seas advanced over the land and the basal deposits are conglomerates and hard sandstones representing the beach deposits of the encroaching sea. These rocks are not fossiliferous but above them come various sandstones, shales and slates with the typical Cambrian fossils.

Cambrian rocks are well exposed in the cliffs around St. Davids in Pembrokeshire. Sandy and shaly rocks at the lower levels indicate fairly shallow seas but fine grained rocks of the Middle Cambrian show a deepening of the water. Return to shallow conditions is shown by the sandy nature of the upper beds. The Tremadoc is missing in South Wales and there is a big unconformity at the base of the Ordovician rocks.

In North Wales, the Harlech Dome is composed of Cambrian rocks which then dip under the Ordovician of Snowdon to reappear in the Llanberis region further north. The beds are very thick – several thousands of feet – but the base is not seen. The lower beds are of coarse pebbles and grits with some shales. There are no fossils, but the rocks are assumed to be Lower Cambrian because *Paradoxides* fossils are found in the overlying shales and slates. The coarse grits are shallow-water deposits and their great thickness – possibly 5,000 feet – means that the area must have been sinking rapidly all the while. There must also have been a region of uplift nearby to

provide all the sediment. The overlying Menevian beds were formed in deeper calmer water, but then shallower conditions returned again as in South Wales.

No Cambrian rocks are found in Anglesey – the Ordovician lies on the pre-Cambrian surface. This region therefore must have been above sea-level during, or immediately after Cambrian times. St. Tudwal's Peninsula, too, was uplifted, for Ordovician rocks lie on Lower Cambrian there. This north-western region of Wales is believed to have been a large rising island responsible for the sediment that was deposited in the sinking region of the Harlech Dome.

The outcrops in Shropshire and the Midlands are of grits, sandstones and shales and are full of unconformities. This area was obviously a shallow-water shelf area and it is likely that land was not far to the south east. The fossils collected from rocks in Germany and Czechoslovakia are very different from the British ones and support the theory of a land barrier.

The fossils of the Scottish Cambrian are also very different from the Welsh ones. They include *Olenellus* and others that are not found in Wales but are found in eastern North America. The Cambrian rocks in Scotland are limestones and shales – very different from the Welsh deposits. Obviously the two regions were separated by a barrier of some sort. The Manx slates on the Isle of Man and various rocks of the Lake District are believed to be Cambrian and suggest that a deep trough (*geosyncline*) ran NE/SW across the British region during Cambrian times. The Harlech geosyncline was a smaller one within the large one.

The scattered outcrops of Cambrian Rock do not provide sufficient evi-

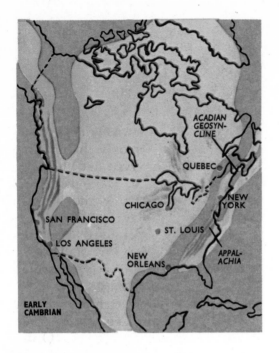

dence for a definite conclusion about the geography of Cambrian times. The accompanying map cannot therefore do more than give a very general idea of what things *may* have been like at that time.

Cambrian North America

North America during the Cambrian Period little resembled its modern appearance. Right from the start shallow seas began to encroach upon the land until one-third of the present-day continent was submerged. These shallow seas did not necessarily correspond to present-day lowlands, but rather to early geosynclines, long depressions in which the foundations of mountain ranges are laid. One corresponded to the present Cordilleran region and another to the present Appalachian region, while a third gradually formed across Oklahoma and Texas. Enclosed by this continental 'moat' was the low, stable interior of the continent. Bordering it were marginal lands of unknown extent. This was the dominant pattern of North America through the Palaeozoic Era. Rocks of the Cambrian System are best exposed in the Canadian Rockies.

CHAPTER SEVENTEEN

The Ordovician Scene

THE early geological maps of Britain showed only three groups of rocks in Wales. These were the *Carboniferous* rocks of the coalfields in the south, the *Old Red Sandstone* of the south-east, and the '*Transition*' rocks which occupied the rest of the country and were supposed to lie on a platform of '*primitive*' rocks.

Sedgwick and Murchison, working in the 1830's, were the first to study the 'Transition' rocks in detail. In North Wales Sedgwick found the base of the 'Transition' rocks and began to work upwards. He named the rocks '*Cambrian*', for Cambria was the Roman name for Wales. Murchison worked farther south at the top of the 'Transition' rocks. He called his rocks '*Silurian*', after the Silures – an ancient tribe of that area.

When the two men compared their results they found that some fossils occurred in both series. It was clear that Sedgwick's 'Upper Cambrian' was equivalent to the 'Lower Silurian' of Murchison. For many years there was argument about what this 'overlapping' part should be called. Charles Lapworth solved the problem in the 1870's. He examined the fossils and suggested that those of the disputed rocks were sufficiently distinct for these rocks to have a separate name. He proposed '*Ordovician*' after another ancient tribe – the Ordovices. The 'Transition' rocks thus became divided into Cambrian, Ordovician and Silurian.

The most characteristic fossils of the Ordovician period are the *grapto-*lites. Nothing is known of the soft parts of the animals, for only the external skeletons are preserved and these are normally squashed. The individual animals were very tiny and lived in cup-shaped structures (skeletons). These 'cups' were arranged in colonies on straight or branched stalks. The graptolites are not clearly related to any living group of animals.

Primitive graptolites first appeared at the end of the Cambrian period. They flourished during the Ordovician and Silurian periods and then died out. During their evolution the shapes of stalk and cup varied a great deal so that many species are recognised. The graptolites are found all over the world and the various species are invaluable in determining the relative ages of rocks, because each species was fairly quickly succeeded by another. Lapworth was able to unravel the structure of the Southern Uplands of Scotland by studying the succession of graptolites. Almost all graptolite fossils are found in deep-sea deposits – now represented mainly by slates and shales. They probably lived as floating colonies – a habit which would have aided rapid distribution.

The lack of graptolites in the sandy and shelly deposits of shallow water may be explained by the fact that their delicate skeletons would be quickly destroyed in the rough conditions close to the shore.

Other important Ordovician fossils are trilobites and the brachiopods which show a much greater range than in the Cambrian. Their shells

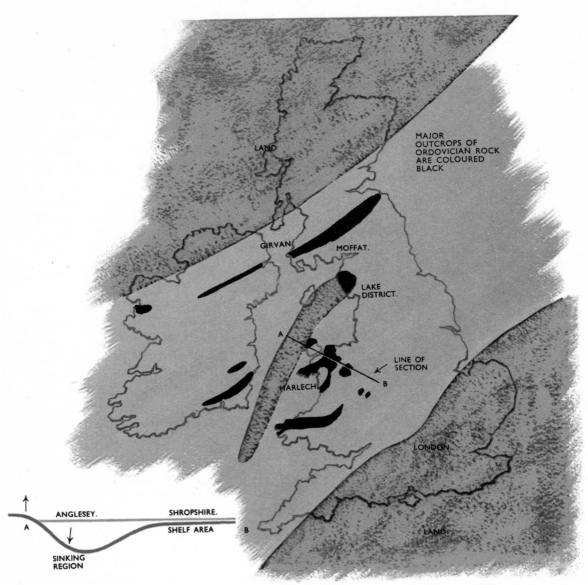

The general features of the region in middle Ordovician times, about 400 million years ago and (inset) a section across Wales to show the geosyncline and the shelf area.

are extremely common in the sandy deposits around the original shore lines. The earliest corals and echinoderms are known from upper Ordovician rocks and these also contain the earliest vertebrates.

Ordovician Britain

The rocks of the Ordovician System lie with some irregularity on those below, indicating folding and uplift at the end of Cambrian times. However, in general the Ordovician Period continued the trend of the Cambrian with deposition centred in a large trough (*geosyncline*) running NE/SW across the region of Britain. In contrast

68

to the preceding period, volcanic activity was widespread, associated with the deepening of the trough. There are great variations in thickness of the Ordovician rocks, due partly to the localised volcanic activity, and partly to the geosynclines where thick deposits accumulated. Thus, while volcanic lavas were forming in one area, black shales were being laid down in another, while yet elsewhere, coarse grits were being deposited in the geosynclines. Ordovician rocks thus show a number of distinct *facies* and it is quite often difficult to relate one outcrop to another.

During the Ordovician Period there was much volcanic activity and uplift and the extent of the sea and its deposits varied considerably.

The lowest division of the system is the *Arenig* whose basal rocks were, in general, laid down in shallow water. They are conglomerates and beach deposits of the encroaching seas. These rocks are overlain by dark shales which were formed in deeper water and contain graptolites. The basal beds of

Anglesey are very thick and coarse and indicate a nearby coastline. The graptolite shales continue from South Wales in a north-easterly direction, through the Lake District and into the Southern Uplands of Scotland. This was the line of the geosyncline. A great deal of volcanic activity went on in South Wales, and in Scotland at this time. Limestones in the north-west of Scotland contain a fossil assemblage very different from that of Wales and the region was obviously cut off as in Cambrian times.

The second division is the *Llanvirn* whose rocks are similar to the shales of the upper Arenig. They contain however, typical 'tuning fork' graptolites with only two branches. In parts of North Wales this zone is represented almost entirely by volcanic rocks. Shales and volcanics are present in Shropshire and in the Lake District the zone is again mainly volcanic. Llanvirn rocks are not found in the Southern Uplands and may never have been deposited. The same is true of the *Llandeilo* beds which elsewhere

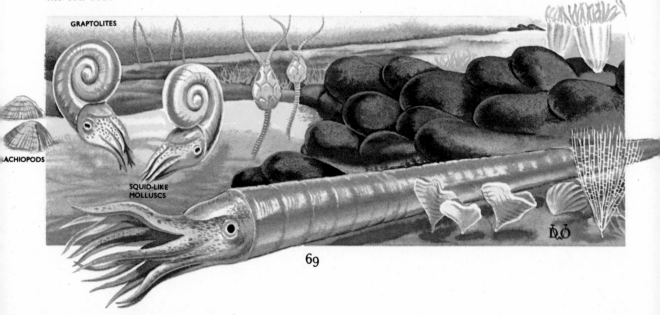

Life in the Ordovician sea. Note the piles of volcanic lava (pillow lava) poured out on to the sea bed.

GRAPTOLITES

BRACHIOPODS

SQUID-LIKE MOLLUSCS

69

lie over the Llanvirn.

The Llandeilo beds are named after a town in South Wales where they consist of sandstones and limestones. This region must have been near the coast, for further west the fine grained graptolitic shales reappear. In Shropshire, the beds are of inter-bedded shelly and graptolitic de-posits – again indicating the nearness of land. In North Wales and the Lake District there was much volcanic activity.

The upper part of the system is the *Bala* division with two series – the *Caradoc* and the *Ashgill*. The latter is missing in Shropshire and Snowdonia because of erosion. The coast was very near to the Longmynd area of Shrop-shire at this time, for the Caradocian sea spread on to much older rocks in this region. Volcanic activity con-tinued during Bala times and lavas are interbedded with shales. Snowdon itself is largely composed of Cara-docian lavas.

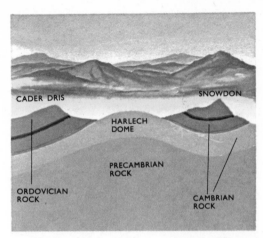

A diagrammatic section across the Harlech dome of Wales showing the relationship of the Cambrian and Ordovician rocks.

The northern coastline of the geo-syncline was close to the Southern Up-land region at this time and there was a sinking area in the region of Girvan. Here, the Bala rocks are very thick grits and greywackes, while the same zones are included in a mere hundred feet of shales at Moffat. This was the quieter, deep water area.

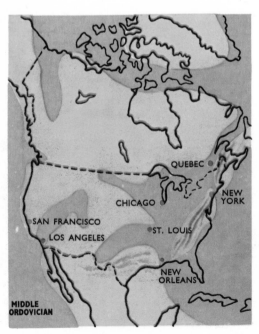

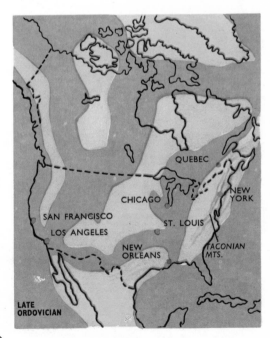

DICHOGRAPTUS
(ARENIG)

DICRANOGRAPTUS
(CARADOC)

Ordovician North America

At the close of Cambrian times the inland seas gradually retreated, forming a natural break in the geological record. But the succeeding period, the Ordovician, which opened some 425 million years ago, brought an even greater submergence. The seas crept in over the low-lying continent until it was reduced to a mass of islands whose total area was only half that of the modern land mass. But in the main the seas were very shallow, and small changes in the land or sea level were sufficient to make the shorelines fluctuate considerably. Twice the continent appears to have emerged from the sea completely, and

thus the Ordovician System, like the Cambrian System, can be divided into three series, the Canadian, Champlainian and Cincinnatian, each with its distinctive fauna. The classic display of these rocks appears in New York State. Most of the marble quarried in the U.S.A. is of Ordovician age, so is most of the slate.

During the Ordovician Period the Taconian Disturbance created the first generation of Appalachians, a range of mountains stretching from Newfoundland to Alabama. But they no longer exist as mountains; the tools of erosion had completed their task of destruction by the middle of the following period.

CHAPTER EIGHTEEN

The Silurian Scene

THE Silurian Period opened approximately 350 million years ago with conditions in Britain closely resembling those of the Ordovician. There were again distinct facies such as the shelly shallow-water deposits, the geosynclinal grits and the deep-water black shales. But volcanoes were no longer active; apart from a few local occurrences, such as in the Mendip Hills, the Silurian remained free from igneous extrusions. Graptolites continued to flourish and remain the most accurate fossils for dating the rocks. Most Ordovician forms had died out but the new, single stranded *Monograptus* appeared and such fossils characterize Silurian rocks. Monograptus and a few relatives were the last graptolites ever to evolve. The

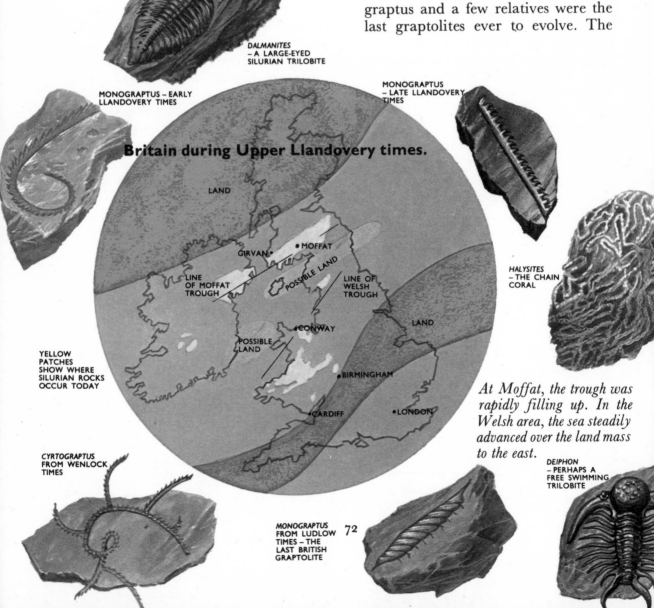

DALMANITES
– A LARGE-EYED
SILURIAN TRILOBITE

MONOGRAPTUS – EARLY
LLANDOVERY TIMES

MONOGRAPTUS
– LATE LLANDOVERY
TIMES

Britain during Upper Llandovery times.

LAND

GIRVAN •   • MOFFAT

LINE
OF MOFFAT
TROUGH

POSSIBLE LAND

LINE OF
WELSH
TROUGH

HALYSITES
– THE CHAIN
CORAL

• CONWAY

LAND

POSSIBLE
LAND

• BIRMINGHAM

YELLOW
PATCHES
SHOW WHERE
SILURIAN ROCKS
OCCUR TODAY

• LONDON

• CARDIFF

At Moffat, the trough was rapidly filling up. In the Welsh area, the sea steadily advanced over the land mass to the east.

DEIPHON
– PERHAPS A
FREE SWIMMING
TRILOBITE

CYRTOGRAPTUS
FROM WENLOCK
TIMES

MONOGRAPTUS
FROM LUDLOW
TIMES – THE
LAST BRITISH
GRAPTOLITE

72

very last species disappeared towards the close of the Silurian, and with it the race became extinct.

In shallow-water, many types of Ordovician trilobite survived but the distinctive *Trinucleus* and *Asaphus* had vanished. Forms with large eyes, such as *Phacops* and *Dalmanites*, became conspicuous. Extremely specialized 'spiny' forms such as *Deiphon* are thought to have been modified for swimming. Brachiopods were numerous and whole banks of shells are preserved where they accumulated on the sea floor. Reef-forming corals flourished, as today, where the seas were clear, and free from muddy sediments. Though not closely related to modern forms, their mode of life appears to have been identical. Thus the Silurian waters in which they grew are thought to have been similar, in depth and temperature, to today's coral seas. In very late Silurian deposits, a few scales and spines show that early fish were just beginning to multiply.

The Silurian period is divided into three stages. First the *Llandovery*, then the *Wenlock* and finally the *Ludlow*. At the start of the Llandovery, the sea in Wales retreated slightly from the land mass to the east, but otherwise, the areas of deposition were much the same as the end of the Ordovician. The geography is accurately known from studies of the rocks themselves. In South Wales at Llandovery, shallow-water sandstones and mudstones with shelly deposits indicate that a coastline lay near to the south-east. Further north-west in Central Wales there are up to 10,000 feet of gritty muds where the trough was situated. Still further north at Conway and Criccieth, in place of this immense thickness of rock, one finds a mere 60 feet of black

shales. This area is thought to have been the centre of the trough remote from any land. It thus received only a very little sediment. The Lake District was directly connected with Wales as proved by the identical fossils. As at Conway, the rocks were thin shales thought to have accumulated far from shore.

Minor earth movements occurred throughout the Llandovery and in Wales the Upper Llandovery sea advanced eastward over the land, as far as Birmingham. The Longmynd Mountain in Shropshire stood out of this sea as an island, for old shingle beaches and sand spits of this age are preserved about it. Similar eastward advances of the sea also took place in the Lake District.

The Llandovery deposits in the Moffat geosyncline in Scotland show some similarity in their fossils to the Welsh rocks. A connection was therefore probable. At Moffat itself, thin shales first accumulated indicating that this area remained the centre of the trough. Girvan, to the north, was still near the shoreline, for great thicknesses of coarse deposits accumulated here. Suddenly at Moffat, thousands of feet of coarse sediments swept right into the trough. Uplift of the land to the north, providing an increased supply of sediments, is thought likely. But at the same time the trough was unable to deepen any more. The rocks became more and more shallow-water types as progressive silting up took place. By the end of the Llandovery, the trough was almost filled. Only a little room was left for deposition in the later Wenlock and Ludlow times.

The Wenlock and Ludlow stages are named after Shropshire towns. In Shropshire itself the sea remained shallow and limestones were precipi-

LIFE IN SILURIAN TIMES

PSILOPHYTES –
EARLY LAND PLANTS

GRAPTOLITE

SQUID-LIKE
MOLLUSC

EURYPTERID – SOME
WERE 6 FEET LONG

Psilophytes, early land plants, lived in late Silurian times. The squid-like mollusc (cephalo-pod) was related to the present-day Nautilus. The Eurypterids, animals related to the scorpions, appeared for the first time in the Silurian seas.

tated from the clear, warm water. Muddy conditions alternated with the limestones, indicating times when sediments were again washed into the area. Today the limestones form the familiar 'edges' of Shropshire with the shales forming intervening valleys. Similar rocks were deposited in Herefordshire, Gloucestershire and as far east as Birmingham. In South Wales there was too much sediment in the seas for pure limestones to develop and calcareous sands and muds were deposited. The last Silurian rocks in Shropshire are sandstones with shallow-water ripple marks. The fossils are stunted, brackish water forms indicating that the area was finally silting up and was probably cut off from the sea.

Westward in the Welsh trough, coarse rocks of enormous thickness accumulated during Wenlock and Ludlow times. Even at Conway, where previously there were only thin shales, sandstones and conglomerates occurred. Further uplifting of a land mass in the present St. George's Channel is thought to have provided a source for these sediments. But again, as at Moffat, the trough was able to sag no more. The deposits built up towards the surface of the sea and by the end of the Silurian, the Welsh geosyncline had become filled. In the Denbigh Moors, in North Wales, Ludlow rocks show actual signs of slumping where the weight of the rapidly accumulating sediments is thought to have caused sliding down steep geosynclinal slopes.

The Lake District has an identical history to that of Wales in Wenlock and Ludlow times. More than 10,000 feet of coarse sediments poured into the trough where previously only shales had been deposited. As in Wales, the trough was filled in by the end of the Silurian.

The silting-up of all three troughs culminated in great earth movements. The geosynclines had been stretched downwards to their limits and filled with sediment. Finally, at the very end of the Silurian, they buckled under the strain. The sediments which had accumulated inside were squashed as

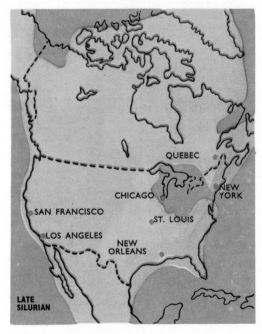

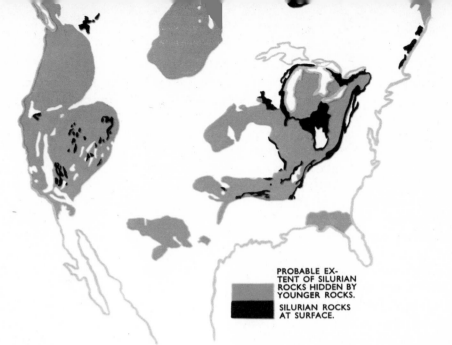

PROBABLE EX-
TENT OF SILURIAN
ROCKS HIDDEN BY
YOUNGER ROCKS.

SILURIAN ROCKS
AT SURFACE.

though in a vice, and folding and faulting still identifiable in these rocks developed. The buckling of the troughs had removed the great pressure in the Earth's crust, and the folded geosynclinal rocks were as a result uplifted. They formed the Caledonian Mountains which provided a source for sediments in the following Devonian period.

Silurian North America

The Silurian Period brought another gradual submergence of North America. The mountains which existed early in the period were gradually worn down and the deposition of fine muds and limestones in the shallow seas indicates generally low-lying land. At the same time, northern Appalachia was the site of active volcanoes which poured out lava and ash with an impressive total thickness of 10,000 feet.

During late Silurian times North America emerged almost completely from the sea, a low-lying, almost featureless land mass. A great desert basin developed in eastern U.S.A. and the rapid evaporation of a shallow sea it contained resulted in the formation of salt and gypsum beds.

Silurian salt beds reach a maximum total thickness of 1,600 feet in Michigan where they are deeply buried beneath the present surface.

The Silurian System of rocks is divided into three series: the Medinan, Niagaran, and Cayugan. Typical rocks of the Middle Silurian are exposed with startling effect at Niagara Falls where a hard, resistant, sill-like mass of limestone, forming the lip of the falls, overlies less resistant shales. Eroded by the undercutting action of the water, the weak shales leave the

HARD LIMESTONE

SHALE

SANDSTONE

Silurian rocks are exposed with startling effect at Niagara Falls.

heavy limestone above jutting out, unsupported, until it crashes down into the gorge beneath. This is why the Niagara Falls have been 'retreating' at the rate of a few feet per year.

CHAPTER NINETEEN

The Devonian Scene

AT the close of the Silurian Period, areas of Britain which for 200 million years had lain under the sea were uplifted into mountains. Sediments were washed out from this new land surface into the sea and accumulated inside yet another trough which had begun to form in the area now known as Devon and Cornwall. Early geologists called the new period the *Devonian* because it is in Devon that the contents of the trough are preserved. The Welsh borderlands and the Central Valley of Scotland were left as two low-lying regions between the new mountains, and there deposits accumulated on the actual land surface, giving a first glimpse of what conditions were like outside the sea.

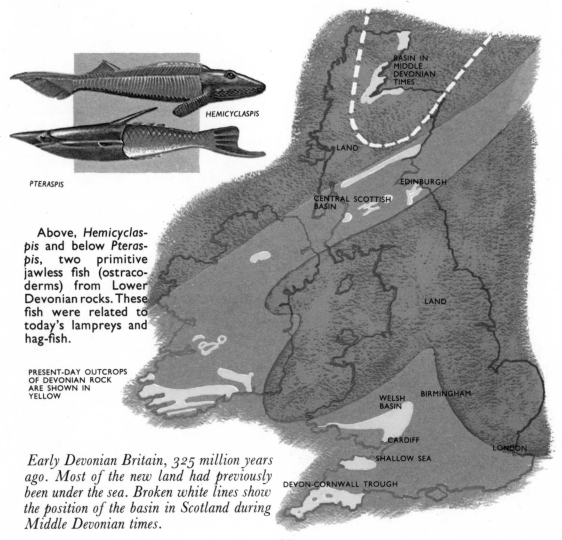

HEMICYCLASPIS

PTERASPIS

Above, *Hemicyclaspis* and below *Pteraspis*, two primitive jawless fish (ostracoderms) from Lower Devonian rocks. These fish were related to today's lampreys and hag-fish.

PRESENT-DAY OUTCROPS OF DEVONIAN ROCK ARE SHOWN IN YELLOW

BASIN IN MIDDLE DEVONIAN TIMES

LAND

EDINBURGH

CENTRAL SCOTTISH BASIN

LAND

BIRMINGHAM

WELSH BASIN

CARDIFF

SHALLOW SEA

LONDON

DEVON-CORNWALL TROUGH

Early Devonian Britain, 325 million years ago. Most of the new land had previously been under the sea. Broken white lines show the position of the basin in Scotland during Middle Devonian times.

The Welsh borderland was at first a shallow marine bay. It slowly filled with sediment and became cut off from the main ocean. The salt content of the enclosed sea water decreased and fewer and fewer marine-living animals could survive. The area was at last turned into a low-lying coastal plain with slow-moving rivers and fresh-water lakes. Sediments of the time have preserved shallow-water ripple marks, and mud-cracks caused by the Sun drying wet clays. Limestone pellets found in the sandstones are believed to have been formed by the evaporation of 'hard' water from pools. Deposits made up of large fragments of rock

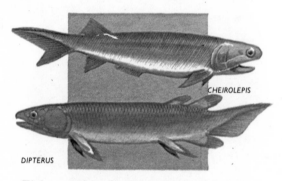

Fish remains found in rocks of Middle Devonian Age. Top: Cheirolepis *belonging to a group from which most later bony fish have descended. Bottom:* Dipterus, *an early lung-fish.*

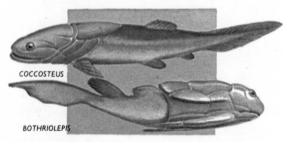

Fish remains found in rocks of Upper Devonian age. Above, Coccosteus *and below* Bothriolepis. *Both were very primitive jawed fish (placoderms) and both became extinct at the end of Devonian times.*

(*conglomerates*) are not common in the area. Conglomerates will accumulate near high land, for large pieces of rock can be moved only by the fast rivers that flow down very steep mountain sides. It is thought therefore that the new mountains in Wales were still rising at this time and were not yet of any great size.

All the sediments that accumulated on the land during the Devonian together make up a sequence of rocks called the *Old Red Sandstone*, though not every rock included is either red or sandy. In the Welsh borderlands, for instance, green and grey sands, muds and silts were deposited amongst the more typical red-stained sediments.

Fish fossils become abundant in Old Red Sandstone rocks. The early forms in the Welsh borderlands were primitive and jawless; they lived on minute plants in the water or dredged in the mud for small organisms. Some seemed able to survive only in fresh-water but others probably lived quite happily in the sea as well. The Ludlow bone bed in the Welsh borderlands is a 'grave yard' of fish. Spines, and fragments of bone making up a layer of rock inches thick, are spread over a wide area. Perhaps it represents a time when a sudden change in the salt content of the water instantaneously destroyed all the fish that were unable to adapt themselves to the new conditions. Evaporation of the water, killing the fish by suffocation, is another possible explanation. Most of the early fish were protected by bony armour – probably a defence against Eurypterid attackers. Eurypterids were large arthropods (some were five or six feet in length), related to scorpions and spiders. They lived both in the sea and in fresh-water during Devonian times.

Life in Devonian seas. The giant fish in the centre is Dinichthys, *a placoderm related to* Coccosteus. *It reached 30 feet in length. Other fish in the picture are early sharks which first appeared in Devonian times.*

To the South, in the trough in Devon, a complete sequence of marine Devonian sediments accumulated – largely grits and mudstones, though on occasions, sediment was small enough in quantity for limestones to be able to develop. Brachiopods (the lamp-shells), made up a very important part of the life in the shallower regions and are used to identify the age of the sediments in which they occur.

North Devon and Somerset was an intermediate area where the sea alternately advanced and retreated, throughout Devonian times. As a result, mixed types of sediment – marine muds and red terrestrial sandstones – occur. Fortunately the rocks are full of fossils and enable the land and sea sediments of the Devonian period to be compared in age.

Scottish Devonian

The Central Valley of Scotland was a sinking basin between lofty mountains. Movement along the Highland boundary fault and the Southern Upland fault, great fractures in the rock which can be seen today, probably started at this time. Certainly the area was unstable, for volcanoes were very active in the basin and also to the south, in the Cheviot Hills. The erosion of the surrounding mountains caused great thicknesses of coarse conglomerates to pour in enormous fans down the hillsides and occasional torrents of rain helped wash the sediments over the valley floor. Lakes in the valley contained fish similar to the types in the Welsh borderlands. Sedge-like land

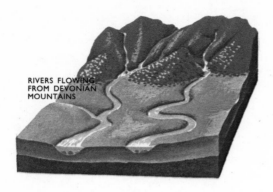

RIVERS FLOWING
FROM DEVONIAN
MOUNTAINS

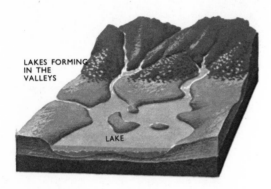

LAKES FORMING
IN THE
VALLEYS

LAKE

MUD-CRACKS
DEVELOPING
IN THE MUDS
OF DRIED UP
LAKES

Block diagrams showing conditions
on the land in Devonian times. Top,
rock fragments are brought from the
mountains by fast rivers. Middle, Lakes
forming on the valley floor. Bottom,
Dried up lakes in times of drought; the
mud cracks are due to the Sun's heat.

plants, the *Psilophytes*, grew on the mud flats near the water.

Younger rocks of Middle Devonian times cannot be recognized either in Wales or Central Scotland. But they are found northwards in Aberdeenshire and Inverness-shire, where a new basin formed. The first sediments were made of coarse rock fragments brought from the mountains that lay to the west. On top of them is a great thickness of fresh-water sands and muds (which are not red in colour) deposited in a curious cyclic rhythm. The first rock is a deep-water mudstone but this becomes coarser and passes upwards into sandstones with shallow-water ripple-marks. There is then a return to deep-water muds again. The alternations could possibly represent seasonal changes. More advanced fishes with jaws, including the ancestors of nearly all today's forms, show that these rocks were deposited later than the rocks of the Welsh borderlands or the Central Valley of Scotland.

At the close of the Middle Devonian there were violent earth movements and further volcanic eruptions. The basins in Central Scotland and Inverness-shire were made into one large structure which probably became connected to the Welsh borderland valley by a long, narrow stretch of inland water. The upper Devonian rocks are chiefly red sandstones deposited in the shallow land-bound waters. The land surface had been slowly reduced to a flat desert-like plain and a large proportion of wind-rounded pebbles and sand grains were blown out into the water. The upper Devonian lakes had their own very distinctive fish, and beds of this age are identified by means of the fish remains.

Devonian North America

The beginning of the Devonian Period in North America marked another invasion by the sea. At first it crept inland along the Appalachian and Cordilleran troughs, but later these narrow straits were reinforced by water spreading southwards across western Canada until possibly 40% of the continent was submerged. Corals

Period, vigorous earth movements brought about renewed uplift in Appalachia. This was the beginning of the Acadian Disturbance which, before the close of the period, created the second generation of Appalachians, stretching from Nova Scotia down to North Carolina. Soon streams began their task of levelling and carried immense amounts of sediment

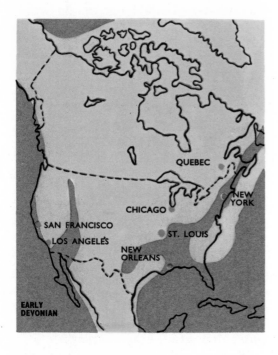

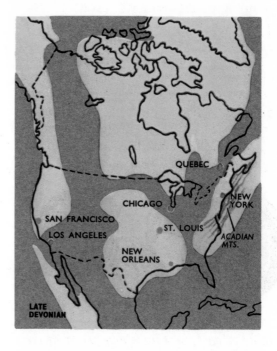

thrived in the clear seas, and since the Silurian Period had left the land low-lying, extensive beds of pure limestone were laid down over the submerged areas.

The Silurian Period had been a quiet one for North America, despite the fact that mountains were being built elsewhere in the world. But, around the middle of the Devonian

down to the neighbouring trough. A tribute to their work is the present-day sandstones of the Catskill Mts. Considerable volcanic activity accompanied the Acadian Disturbance.

The Devonian System, which is divided into a lower, middle and upper series, is best exposed in the state of New York where it reaches the impressive total thickness of 15,000 feet.

CHAPTER TWENTY

The Carboniferous Scene

THE Carboniferous Period which began some 280,000,000 years ago has a tremendous present-day significance, for it is to the conditions which existed then that we owe one of our greatest mineral assets – coal. Warm, moist sub-tropical climates in North America, Europe, Asia and elsewhere enabled luxuriant forests to grow in vast swamps, though the trees were very unlike forms now in existence. When they died the plant remains fell into the stagnant swamp water. This ancient vegetation has formed the coal seams of today.

RETICULOCERAS —GONIATITES

Fossil goniatites (free-swimming relatives of the squid) are used to date deep-water and muddy sediments.

Coal formed only at certain episodes of Carboniferous history – mainly in late or *Upper Carboniferous* times. In the earlier *Lower Carboniferous* times the rocks formed were mostly limestones.

Lower Carboniferous

The British Isles at the close of the Devonian Period were almost flat; the Caledonian Mts. of Wales and Southern Scotland had been worn down to stumps. The early Carboniferous sea advanced first from the south into Wales and much of South-West England, and then from the west into much of Northern England. The low-lying lands provided very little sediment and pure limestones were deposited from the shallow, warm seas. Scotland still stood out of the water and the earliest Carboniferous sandstones there, were formed in fresh-water lakes.

Violent earth-movements (*Bretonian*) with strong volcanic activity interrupted this early peaceful episode. When they were over, the sea had flooded more areas at the edge of the land mass. All Northern England, North Wales and parts of South Scotland were submerged while the lagoons in the Scottish Central Valley area were frequently flooded by invasions of the sea. The movements also uplifted parts of the Welsh land-mass. Sands weathered from this new, high surface poured into the seas both to the north and to the south, interrupting the limestone deposition in many places.

Parts of the sea floor in Northern England became very unstable. Rapidly sinking basins in Lancashire, Derbyshire and Nottinghamshire accumulated great thicknesses of shales with only thin, impure limestones. Similar sediments were also settling in the Devon-Cornwall trough to the south. The Lake District and much of the Pennine area was stable, subsiding far more slowly. Thick, pure limestones developed in these regions and continued to form in the stable shallow seas over parts of South and North Wales, Bristol and the Mendip area.

Northumberland lay very near to

COAL SWAMP

C SANDS WITH PEBBLES

ONAL MUDS

E MUDS

MARINE FOSSILS

PTERINOPECTEN

SILIZED SOIL (SEAT-EARTH)
H 'ROOTS' IN POSITION
GROWTH

FISH
TEETH

GASTRIOCERAS

ANTHRACONAUTA—A FRESH-WATER
BIVALVE

A coal swamp of Upper Carboniferous times. The rhythmic sedimentation shows the earlier history of the region. A previous swamp is indicated by a lower coal seam. Invasion of the sea followed, depositing mud with marine fossils. Before the delta returned, there was an intermediate lagoonal stage.

the land in Scotland. It represented an intermediate area with stable periods alternating with periods of rapid subsidence. The sedimentation is as a result *rhythmic;* deep-water and shallow-water deposits continually alternate.

Very slow subsidence meant the area became choked with sediment brought by rivers from the north. There was little current activity to disperse the piled-up deposits and a delta grew out of the water as has happened at the mouth of to-day's River Nile. Luxuriant, sub-tropical forests soon established themselves on the delta. Further subsidence caused the sea to return, destroying the forests. But the remains of dead plants are preserved as coal seams. This was the first Carboniferous coal-forming area. Coal formation on a larger scale was to take place in the Upper Carboniferous.

Upper Carboniferous

Another phase of violent earthmovements (*Sudetic*) caused more changes in the geography. This phase

Coal was formed from woody plant remains that fell into stagnant, swampy waters. The lack of oxygen prevented normal decomposition from taking place. Instead, partial decay by the action of *anaerobic* bacteria removed only oxygen. The carbon proportion was subsequently increased – from about 44% to about 60%. Similar peaty layers are at present forming in the Everglade swamps of Florida.

Slight subsidence caused the sea to invade the delta, preserving the peaty layer under marine sediments. But more weathered fragments from the land soon built up the delta and new forests reappeared. Subsequently more peat was developed.

Increase of pressure and temperature under the weight of overlying rocks steadily increased the carbon proportion and have turned the peaty layers into coal seams. The best coal (*anthracite*) is made up of 95% carbon.

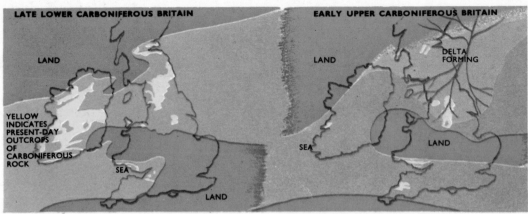

LAND

YELLOW
INDICATES
PRESENT-DAY
OUTCROPS
OF
CARBONIFEROUS
ROCK

SEA

LAND

LAND

DELTA
FORMING

SEA

LAND

Limestones formed in the Pennine area, South Wales and Bristol. Deeper-water shales accumulated in Lancashire and Devon.

Mud brought down from the north by rivers, built up a huge delta. A small delta also formed in Wales.

of mountain-building separates the Lower Division of the Carboniferous from the Upper. The large-scale formation of limestone came to a halt.

The whole of the Scottish Midland Valley and the Southern Uplands subsided, becoming a large delta stretching out from the land mass of North Scotland. Northumberland made up just part of this delta.

Elsewhere in Northern England, the sea was at first fairly open, depositing shales and thin limestones. But the Scottish delta slowly extended southwards. Vast quantities of sands and pebbles were brought down from the northern land mass by great rivers. These sediments form the coarse sandstone known as the *Millstone Grit.*

The whole delta was occasionally re-invaded by the sea. This is known from layers of shale containing marine fossils. At first, the only coal formed was in the Scottish section of the delta. Elsewhere the grits formed barren, flat expanses. Very similar conditions led to delta formations also in South Wales and near Bristol.

Slowly the deltaic flats turned into vast swamps covered with luxuriant vegetation. These were the times when most of our coal seams were formed. The trees grew in several inches of water but were well adapted to such conditions. Their roots are often found to-day preserved in fossilized soil just as they grew in life. Periodically the swamps were flooded by the sea destroying the forest but preserving the layers of dead plant remains.

The submergence of the swamps coincided with further uplift of the land surface. This provided new supplies of sediment for building the delta up out of the sea again.

In addition to the large deltas of Northern England and Scotland, deltas in South Wales and in the Bristol area provided swamps suitable for coal development. The swamps evidently stretched over much of Southern England for coal seams of

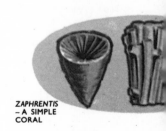

ZAPHRENTIS
– A SIMPLE
CORAL

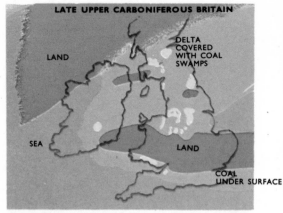

DELTA COVERED WITH COAL SWAMPS

LAND

SEA

LAND

COAL UNDER SURFACE

Coal forests covered the extensive swampy deltas. The deltas were occasionally invaded by the sea.

Upper Carboniferous age are found as far east as Kent.

Carboniferous North America

Despite the differences between Lower and Upper Carboniferous rocks they are generally recognised in Europe as belonging to one system – the Carboniferous. In North America, however, the differences are considered sufficient to justify two systems and hence two periods – the Mississippian (Lower Carboniferous) and the Pennsylvanian (Upper Carboniferous).

At the opening of the Mississippian Period (Lower Carboniferous) 280 million years ago North America was fully emergent, but soon the sea invaded the land and the Mississippi Valley in particular remained submerged throughout the period. Hence, the Mississippian System is fairly complete in this region, where it con-

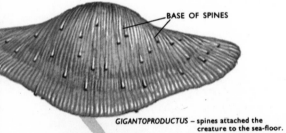

BASE OF SPINES

GIGANTOPRODUCTUS – spines attached the creature to the sea-floor.

Typical Carboniferous limestone country. The rocks contain numerous brachiopods, many corals, spiny-skinned echinoderms, bivalves and tube-like bryozones.

SCARPS FORMED BY MILLSTONE GRIT

STROTION
OMPOUND
L

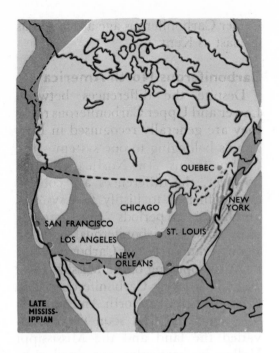

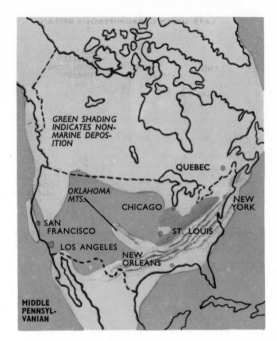

sists mainly of uniform rich fossiliferous limestone strata attaining a maximum total thickness of 2,500 feet.

Towards the close of the Mississippian Period widespread earth movements disturbed North America and the land began to rise not only in Appalachia but also in Colorado. This was just a foretaste of disturbances which were to culminate in the Appalachian Revolution at the close of the era.

During the Pennsylvanian Period (Upper Carboniferous), which opened 255 million years ago, a broad basin slowly formed over the interior of the U.S.A. Then a battle developed between the encroaching sea and river-borne sediment, derived from the mountains in Appalachia, as the land slowly sank. Sometimes the sea advanced eastwards, right to Pennsylvania at one point, while at other times deposition more than balanced subsidence and the shore line was pushed back to the Rocky Mountain states. The result was the development of vast swampy lowlands covered with lush vegetation and the ultimate creation of North America's great coal deposits.

Continued crustal unrest during this period resulted in the uplift of the Oklahoma Mountains, the vestiges of which can now be seen in the Wichita and Arbuckle Mountains. Uplift also occurred in Colorado, and resulted in the creation of a fairly low mountain range. Near the end of the period the Marathon Disturbance created a range of mountains across Texas.

CHAPTER TWENTY-ONE

The Permian Scene

THE Permian Period began after intense movements – the so-called *Armorican* movements – had shaken the Earth at the close of the Carboniferous (coal-forming) period. Most of North-West Europe became lifted out of the water and the open sea of the time lay far to the south in the Mediterranean region. In Britain the most important effect of the movements was to fold the rocks of South Wales, and much of South-West England. The direction of the pressure came from the north and the arches of folded rock, (*anticlines*) such as are found in the Mendip hills, run in an east-west direction.

A very dry Permian climate turned much of the new land mass into desert. As happens in existing deserts, the hot days and cool nights caused alternate expansion and contraction in rocks and fragments soon broke off along planes of weakness. The pieces from the mountains built up fans which moved down into the valleys, occasionally assisted by torrential rain storms. Smaller particles were blown about by the wind and today they form red sandstones.

In Britain there were two low-lying areas where sediments could accumulate – a small basin in Devon and a wide plain stretching northwards from mountains in the English Midlands to Southern Scotland and Northern Ireland. Volcanic eruption poured lava flows over the desert floors of Scotland.

In late Permian times much of Northern England became the western margin of an inland sea. This so-called *Zechstein sea* was centred over Germany and resembled the present Dead Sea of Jordan. The water was

Areas of deposition in late Permian times.

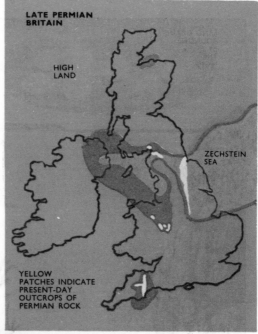

LATE PERMIAN BRITAIN

HIGH LAND

ZECHSTEIN SEA

YELLOW PATCHES INDICATE PRESENT-DAY OUTCROPS OF PERMIAN ROCK

ELSEWHERE IN THE WORLD, PERMO-TRIASSIC REPTILE REMAINS ARE MORE PLENTIFUL. THIS AMERICAN THECODONT WAS 15 FOOT LONG

APPALACHIAN PLATEAU

RIDGE AND VALLEY BELT

GREAT VALLEY

BLUE R

NORTH-WEST

FOLDED SEDIMENTARY ROCKS (CAMBRIAN-CARBONIFEROUS)

A schematic cross-section of the southern Appalachians.

very salty; some salt was probably derived from drainage of the land but enrichment also took place when the open sea that lay in the present Mediterranean region occasionally broke in through a narrow entrance. Animal life in the water consisted of brachiopods, bivalves and tube-like,

reef-forming bryozoa. Because of the very salty conditions these animals were exceptionally small, stunted forms.

Evaporation of the Zechstein sea often removed water faster than it could be supplied from the land, and as a result, salts (*evaporites*) were

Erosion in a Permian desert. Rock screes slide down the mountains while the wind blows sand as dunes about the desert floor. The blue of the Zechstein sea can be seen in the far distance.

SAND GRAINS ROUNDED BY THE WIND

PEBBLES SCULPTURED BY WIND-DRIVEN SAND

SCREE

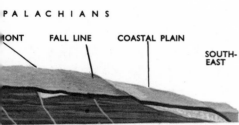

PALACHIANS

ONT   FALL LINE   COASTAL PLAIN

SOUTH-
EAST

HRUST CRYSTALLINE ROCKS

a violent and spectacular close. The Appalachian geosyncline had existed to a greater or lesser degree ever since Pre-Cambrian times and by this time over *forty thousand feet* of rock strata had accumulated on its slowly subsiding floor. Then, during this period, Appalachia was pushed from the south-east against the geosyncline

thrown out of solution. The order in which salts are precipitated depends upon their solubility in water. Dolomites and limestones are the least soluble and appear first. They are followed by anhydrite, gypsum, and finally rock-salt and salts of potassium.

Each time evaporation took place, Yorkshire and Nottinghamshire which were on an extreme western margin, duly received a coating of dolomite and gypsum. By the time the potassium salts were thrown out of solution, the diminishing water lay further eastwards towards the centre of the sea. Consequently British Upper Permian rocks outcropping in the area include dolomites and limestones with only occasional gypsum, and rock-salt bands. Borings further eastward have revealed increasingly thicker salt deposits under the surface.

The thickest formation of dolomites (up to 800 feet) forms a ridge along the east side of the Pennines. The Zechstein sea however penetrated to the west of the Pennines and spread as far as Ireland. Thin dolomite layers were formed on top of red windblown sands of early Permian age.

Permian North America

The Permian Period brought the Palaeozoic Era in North America to

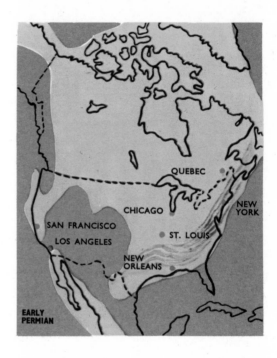

and the rocks it contained were squeezed as if in a giant vice. Buckled and fractured, they were forced into a mountain chain which rivalled the present Alps in height and extended down the eastern seaboard as far as Alabama. In some places the rocks of the geosyncline had been deformed by earlier disturbances but, in the main, the structure of the Appalachians dates from this mountain-building phase.

Early in the period a large part

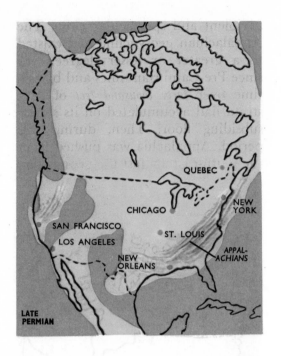

of the mid-continent lowland was submerged, shallow seas reaching as far north as Nebraska and Ohio. But gradually the outlet of the sea was cut off through the warping of the land and the deposition of sediment, leaving a vast inland sea which slowly dried up, owing to the very arid climate. The last remnant of the sea was in the present state of Kansas where extensive salt beds were formed. Important changes were also taking place in the West, where volcanoes were extremely active.

The Permian System (including the Wolcampian, Leonardian, Guadalupian, and Ochoan Series) is extremely well developed in western Texas where it attains a thickness of 14,000 feet.

The Mesozoic World

CHAPTER TWENTY-TWO

The Triassic Scene

TWO hundred million years ago, a new era, the Mesozoic, began in the Earth's long history. This was the time when reptiles really came into their own. The following 130 million years witnessed the rise of reptilian forms until they dominated the land, the sea and the air. Most spectacular and certainly best known are the dinosaurs. Most (but not all) of these were large, and some forms reached the colossal weight of 50 tons. The name 'dinosaur', which literally means 'terrible lizard', is a very broad one which really includes two orders of reptiles, the *Saurischia*, *e.g.*, *Allosaurus* and *Brontosaurus*, and the *Ornithischia*, *e.g.*, *Stegosaurus* and *Trachydon*.

The Triassic Period, the first division of the Mesozoic Era, was something of an anti-climax in North America. The tumultuous close of the preceding era had seen the creation of a great mountain range in the east (the Appalachians), and the first part of the Triassic Period was marked by continuous erosion as streams and rivers began their task of erasing this wrinkle in the land surface. But later in the period extensive faulting and uplifting in the Appalachian region (the *Palisade Disturbance*) created a narrow chain of tilted block mountains, bordered by deep troughs. As these troughs were being formed the deposition of sediment derived from the neighbouring highlands continued apace on their subsiding floors. Hence they now contain a rich record

AREAS OF
NON-MARINE
DEPOSITION

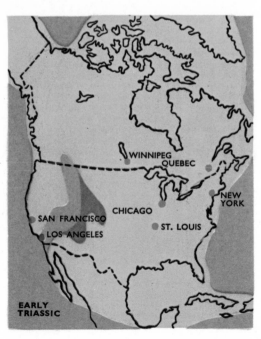

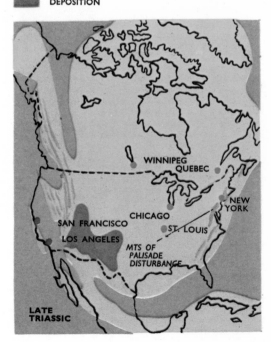

Dimetrodon – *a flesh-eating, fin-backed reptile, seizes a young* Ophiacodon. *The scene could well have been eastern U.S.A. at the dawn of the Mesozoic Era.*

A scene in Triassic times. A 4-foot long reptile (a thecodont) *which walked on two legs leaves a trail of footprints to be fossilized. The small lizard is a close relative of today's sphenodon.*

of Upper Triassic rocks collectively termed the Newark group. These strata exceed 20,000 feet in thickness locally.

In the present Rocky Mountain region continental deposits were being laid down over a wide area under arid conditions. The red and purple shales and sandstones thus formed now produce the spectacular scenery of the Painted Desert, Arizona. In the Far West a seaway reached from California to southern Canada early in the period and in it were deposited shales and limestones rich in fossils.

The Triassic Period saw the beginning of a new pattern in North America. In the west a broad belt of land from Utah and Nebraska to Canada was slowly being uplifted and either side of it geosynclines were developing – the Pacific Coast geosyncline to the west and the Rocky Mountain geosyncline to the east (geosynclines are long trough-like depressions in which the foundations of mountain ranges are laid).

Britain in Triassic Times

The Triassic Period derives its title from a German word meaning three-layered. In Germany two layers of land-deposited sediment are separated by a marine episode. But this invasion of the sea never penetrated as far west as Britain and the British Trias rocks all accumulated on land. The area in which they were deposited was a considerably extended version of the Permian lowlands. Hence the red rocks from both periods are remarkably alike in appearance and a lack of fossils makes it difficult to separate them.

In early Trias times (called the *Bunter*) pebbles and cobbles were still eroded from the highlands. The Trias climate had become wetter and the pebbles were rounded by river action. The pebbles, unlike the larger fragments in Permian rocks, are not just concentrated near the high land of the time. They have been spread over wide areas by occasional, swollen rivers. An interest-

94

ing geological study is to relate the different types of pebble with possible parent rocks still in existence today.

By late Trias Times (called the *Keuper*) the Armorican hills were disappearing. The most common rock is a fine-grained, red sediment. It was formed from very fine clay and silt particles dispersed by the wind, and deposited on the desert floor or in temporary lakes.

Temporary lakes often formed as a result of occasional torrential rain. Rain water dissolved salt from the land and the lakes were salty. The subsequent evaporation of the water by the hot sun left behind concentrations of gypsum and rock-salt. These are today exploited in Cheshire, Lancashire, Worcestershire and Somerset.

Right at the end of the Triassic period, the fine-grained sediments lost their red colour and became green; red ferric salts were reduced to green ferrous salts in a very much wetter climate.

Areas of deposition in late Triassic times

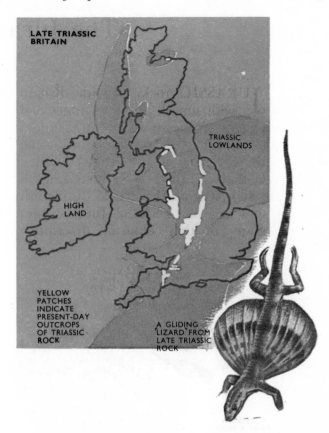

LATE TRIASSIC BRITAIN

TRIASSIC LOWLANDS

HIGH LAND

YELLOW PATCHES INDICATE PRESENT-DAY OUTCROPS OF TRIASSIC ROCK

A GLIDING LIZARD FROM LATE TRIASSIC ROCK

For land creatures to be fossilized, they have to be quickly buried as shown in this Triassic scene.

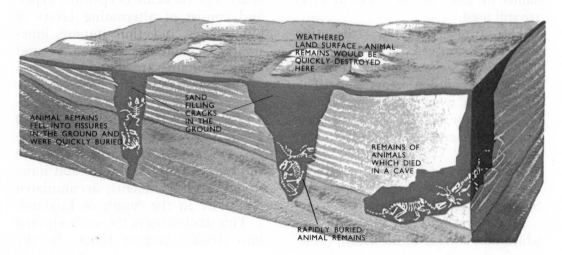

WEATHERED LAND SURFACE – ANIMAL REMAINS WOULD BE QUICKLY DESTROYED HERE

SAND FILLING CRACKS IN THE GROUND

ANIMAL REMAINS FELL INTO FISSURES IN THE GROUND AND WERE QUICKLY BURIED

REMAINS OF ANIMALS WHICH DIED IN A CAVE

RAPIDLY BURIED ANIMAL REMAINS

CHAPTER TWENTY-THREE

The Jurassic Scene

JURASSIC rocks provide Britain with superb building stones and valuable iron ores. They also contain a large variety of fossils including the remains of monstrous reptiles. William Smith – the famous English geologist – was the first to distinguish and map the rocks of Jurassic age; many of the colourful descriptive

PLEUROCERAS LIVED IN LIAS TIMES

PARKINSONIA WAS A MIDDLE JURASSIC AMMONITE

Jurassic ammonites evolved rapidly and were widely distributed. They are very important for relating the rocks.

names he gave to the rocks in 1799 are still used.

The Jurassic period (the title *Jurassic* is derived from the *Jura Mountains* of Switzerland and France) began 170 million years ago. The rocks which were formed in Britain outcrop at the surface in a broad belt which stretches from the Dorset coast to the North Yorkshire coast. They dip gently eastwards and are present under later rocks in most parts of South and East England.

At the end of Trias times the sea, which had lain far to the south, broke in and flooded the flat deserts that then covered the British Isles. At first the salty water lay on the surface as lagoons, and sediments of the *Rhaetic* episode accumulated. Rhaetic rocks are never very thick; they consist of grey shales and thin limestones and contain a *bone* bed – probably the remains of reptiles which were drowned when the sea first invaded the land. (Some geologists group Rhaetic rocks with continental Triassic rocks, others group them with the predominantly marine deposits of the Jurassic period.)

Thereafter, the depth of the sea floor varied continually. In deep waters, muds and clays could settle, but in shallow water the light particles were disturbed by wave action and only larger, heavier grains of sand and limestone remained.

Lower and Middle Jurassic Times

The *Lower Jurassic* (not including the Rhaetic rocks) is called the *Lias* – a quarryman's corruption of the word *layers*. The rocks are deep-water types, and consist of alternating layers of blue shales and thin impure limestones. Spectacular ammonites and reptile remains are found entombed in these sediments and are especially famous from the cliffs of Dorset.

The Lias rocks form a low belt of good agricultural land stretching across England. Towards the top of the Lias the sea shallowed, and limestones and sediments accumulated especially in the South of England.

This shallowing of the sea continued into *Middle Jurassic* times. In the

96

Cotswold Hills, the thick limestones form a steep escarpment overlooking the Severn Valley. The limestones are *oolitic* – they are made up of numerous small spheres resembling fish-eggs (Greek, *oon* an egg, *lithos* a stone). Each 'egg' consists of a small sand grain or shell fragment that was rolled about the Jurassic sea-floor and became coated with the limestone precipitated from the warm seas.

Followed southwards into Somerset and Dorset, Middle Jurassic rocks are deeper water deposits; the limestones are thin and there is much more muddy sediment giving gently rolling hills rather than strong escarpments.

Northwards, Middle Jurassic rocks are sandier and, in Northampton, are important as iron-stones (mined in open-cast workings) but limestones make up the prominent *Lincolnshire Edge*.

In the very north of Yorkshire there is a spectacular change in landscape. Middle Jurassic rocks form the bleak, barren Yorkshire Moors and Cleveland Hills. The rocks are mostly sands, with thin mud-layers and coal seams. Here was a delta in

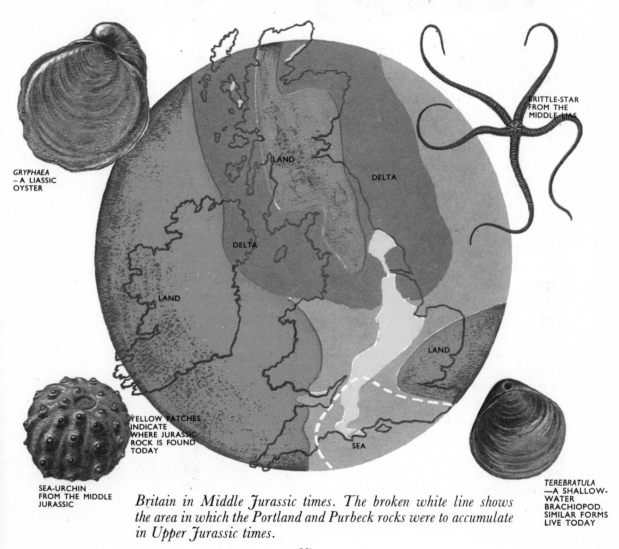

GRYPHAEA – A LIASSIC OYSTER

BRITTLE-STAR FROM THE MIDDLE LIAS

LAND

DELTA

DELTA

LAND

LAND

YELLOW PATCHES INDICATE WHERE JURASSIC ROCK IS FOUND TODAY

SEA

SEA-URCHIN FROM THE MIDDLE JURASSIC

TEREBRATULA —A SHALLOW-WATER BRACHIOPOD. SIMILAR FORMS LIVE TODAY

Britain in Middle Jurassic times. The broken white line shows the area in which the Portland and Purbeck rocks were to accumulate in Upper Jurassic times.

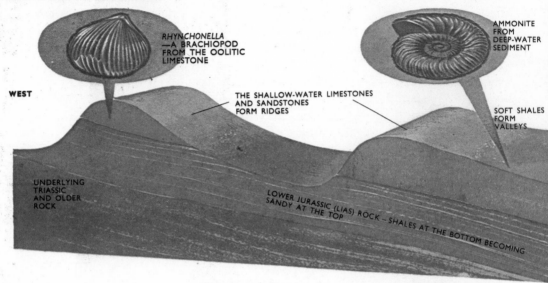

East-west section through Jurassic rocks of Southern England showing the order in which Jurassic sediments accumulated.

RHYNCHONELLA —A BRACHIOPOD FROM THE OOLITIC LIMESTONE

AMMONITE FROM DEEP-WATER SEDIMENT

WEST

THE SHALLOW-WATER LIMESTONES AND SANDSTONES FORM RIDGES

SOFT SHALES FORM VALLEYS

UNDERLYING TRIASSIC AND OLDER ROCK

LOWER JURASSIC (LIAS) ROCK – SHALES AT THE BOTTOM BECOMING SANDY AT THE TOP

Middle Jurassic times, built up of coarse sediment brought from surrounding land masses. The delta was very similar to those of the Carboniferous period and likewise supported forests, though the trees were much more like present-day forms than the Carboniferous ones. Unfortunately, coal formation did not take place on a large scale. In Scotland a few patches of deltaic sandstone have also been preserved.

Upper Jurassic Times

William Smith called the first Upper Jurassic rock the *Cornbrash* because this thin, blue limestone band breaks down to give an excellent soil for growing corn. The Cornbrash can be traced from Dorset to North Yorkshire and as it is a marine rock with marine fossils, evidently the Yorkshire delta had become submerged. An influx of sand formed the succeeding *Kellaway Rock*, but then the sea deepened (except in Yorkshire) for the following *Oxford Clay* was formed in deep water.

Again the sea shallowed and the next rock, the *Corallian*, is in most places limey or sandy and contains fossilized coral reefs. This was followed by the last deep-water Jurassic episode – represented by the thick blue *Kimmeridge Clay*. Finally the *Portland* and *Purbeck* rocks were formed. By this time the area of deposition had shrunk to a small bay covering South-East England. Rocks of *Portland* age are mostly thick, oolitic limestones famous as building stones. Quarries on Portland Bill, Dorset, have provided much of the stone used in the buildings of London.

The Jurassic period opened with

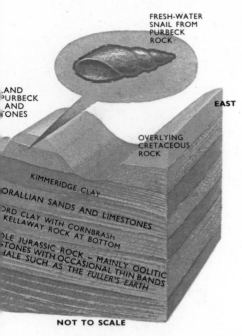

FRESH-WATER
SNAIL FROM
PURBECK
ROCK

EAST

...AND
...PURBECK
...AND
...TONES

OVERLYING
CRETACEOUS
ROCK

KIMMERIDGE CLAY

...ORALLIAN SANDS AND LIMESTONES

...RD CLAY WITH CORNBRASH
...KELLAWAY ROCK AT BOTTOM

...LE JURASSIC ROCK — MAINLY OOLITIC
...TONES WITH OCCASIONAL THIN BANDS
...ALE SUCH AS THE FULLER'S EARTH

NOT TO SCALE

invasion of the sea. It closed with the sea once more driven back to the south. *Purbeck* rocks are fresh-water muds and limestones with little marine sediment. Most startling are the '*dirt*' *beds*, or fossilized soils, with tree stumps in their original position of growth.

Jurassic North America

The Jurassic Period in North America saw the development of the pattern which began to take shape in the preceding period. East of the rising highland belt the sea spread southwards as the Rocky Mountain geosyncline slowly developed. Eventually, during the latter part of the period, the land as far east as central North Dakota and as far south as New Mexico was submerged. But later still the sea retreated and the former sea bed became a fertile lowland, clothed with luxuriant vegetation and crossed by numerous sluggish rivers flowing down from the highlands to the west. These spread large quantities of mud and gravel across the area, producing the present-day Morrison formation which extends from Colorado in the east to Utah in the west, and from New Mexico in the south to Montana in the north. Consisting mainly of shales and sandstones, this formation rarely exceeds 400 feet in thickness but it contains a marvellous record of Jurassic land animals and plants, including seventy species of dinosaurs and twenty-five species of primitive mammals. The moist lowland region where these rocks were laid down had a wide variety of animal life and the rapid deposition of sediment by countless meandering rivers provided unusually favourable conditions for fossilization. The Morrison formation is difficult to date accurately, for its

Middle Jurassic landscape in Yorkshire. The area was a delta covered with vegetation. The creature in the air is a pterosaur – a flying reptile.

99

assemblage of fossils is unique in North America. But comparison with similar rocks in other continents suggests Late Jurassic.

Meanwhile, the other great depression which had made its appearance in the Triassic Period, the Pacific Coast geosyncline, continued to deepen throughout most of the Jurassic Period and received a large amount of sediment from rivers flow-ing off the highlands to the east. Between the two geosynclines earth movements, which had already uplifted the land slightly in the preceding period, grew steadily in intensity throughout the Jurassic Period and finally culminated in the first great spasm of the Alpine Revolution (the Nevadian Disturbance) which created a range of fold mountains in place of the highlands.

CHAPTER TWENTY-FOUR

The Cretaceous Scene

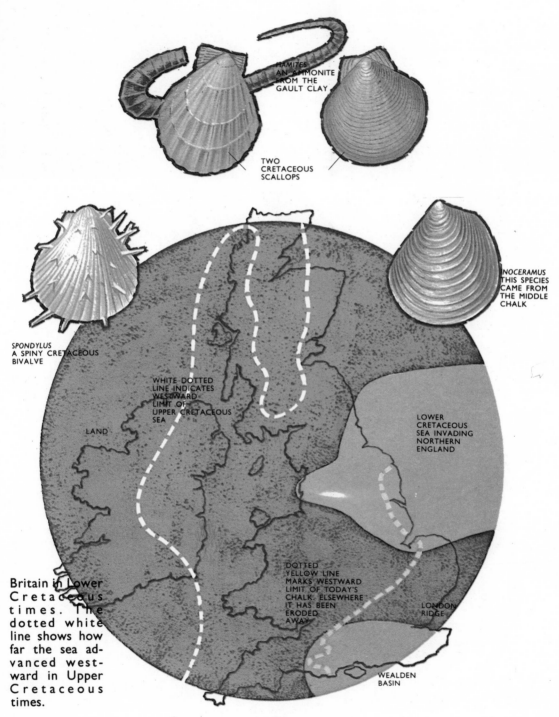

HAMITES
AN AMMONITE
FROM THE
GAULT CLAY

TWO
CRETACEOUS
SCALLOPS

INOCERAMUS
THIS SPECIES
CAME FROM
THE MIDDLE
CHALK

SPONDYLUS
A SPINY CRETACEOUS
BIVALVE

WHITE DOTTED
LINE INDICATES
WESTWARD
LIMIT OF
UPPER CRETACEOUS
SEA

LAND

LOWER
CRETACEOUS
SEA INVADING
NORTHERN
ENGLAND

DOTTED
YELLOW LINE
MARKS WESTWARD
LIMIT OF TODAY'S
CHALK. ELSEWHERE
IT HAS BEEN
ERODED
AWAY

LONDON
RIDGE

Britain in Lower
Cretaceous
times. The
dotted white
line shows how
far the sea ad-
vanced west-
ward in Upper
Cretaceous
times.

WEALDEN
BASIN

Birds-eye view of Eastern England in Lower Cretaceous times. In the foreground the Wealden delta was built in fresh water. Northwards the sea invaded Lincolnshire and Yorkshire.

WEALDEN
DELTA
WITH SWAMPS, RIVERS, LAKES AND POOLS

A PTERODACTYL
– SUCH FLYING
REPTILES FILLED
THE CRETACEOUS
SKIES

IGUANODON
A 14-FOOT HIGH PLANT-
EATING
DINOSAUR OF
CRETACEOUS
TIMES

AN ELASMOSAUR – A GIANT
SEA-DWELLING
CRETACEOUS REPTILE

*At the end of Cretaceous times
the dinosaurs and other great
reptiles became extinct.*

SEA IN NORTH-EAST ENGLAND

THE LONDON RIDGE – HIGH GROUND COVERED WITH FORESTS

THE Cretaceous period derives its title from the Latin word, *creta*, meaning chalk. Chalk is a dazzling white, very pure limestone (limestone is made of calcium carbonate) and in Britain forms the Wolds of Lincolnshire and Yorkshire as well as the Chiltern Hills and the Downs of Southern England. Along the coasts, it outcrops as spectacular white cliffs and where it is worked for lime, the quarries appear as white cuttings in the green hillsides.

Chalk was formed in the clear warm seas that lay over most of Britain in Upper Cretaceous times. In Lower Cretaceous times the conditions were very different; so were the sediments.

Lower Cretaceous Times

At the start of the Cretaceous period 130 million years ago, most of Britain was land. The site of London stood on a ridge which ran eastwards into Belgium, westwards into the English Midlands. South of the ridge lay a shallow, fresh-water basin – the same basin in which the last Jurassic rocks had accumulated. Northwards in Lin-colnshire and Yorkshire, a new sea had invaded the land from the east.

The sediments of these two areas, though of the same age, are of completely different types. To the south, they are alternating sands and shales (*Wealden Beds*) which were laid down as a delta by rivers draining the London ridge and land masses of Western England and Wales. Some of the sediment, especially the clays, was deposited in deeper water, probably after the delta floor had suddenly subsided. There were times, however, when sediment accumulated to such an extent that the delta emerged out of the water. Preserved in sandstone slabs are impressions of rain pits, and reptilian foot marks as well as ripple marks (made in shallow water) and sun-cracks. Swamps even formed, for fossil soil beds with ancient relatives of todays' horsetails are known.

While giant reptiles such as *Iguanodon* strode about on the sandy flats and in the swampy waters of the Wealden delta, a blue marine clay (*Speeton Clay*) with fossil ammonites accumulated in the seas over Yorkshire.

A strong advance of the ocean must next have taken place. The delta covering the Weald and much of Hampshire and Dorset became submerged under salt water as the sea encroached upon the London ridge from the south. To the north, the sea similarly advanced and the two seas finally joined in a narrow corridor at the western margin of the ridge.

In Southern England, the sediment laid down in the shallow water is known as the *Lower Greensand*. In places there are indeed sandstones with a greenish tinge (caused by traces of a green mineral called *glauconite*). But in general, the sediments are so variable in type, colour and thickness that the title is used only for convenience. To the north of the London ridge the rocks equivalent in age to the Wealden 'Lower Greensand' are yellow sands, especially thick in Norfolk and Bedfordshire.

Another great advance of the sea followed, probably almost submerging the London ridge and extending as far West as Dartmoor and possibly Wales.

Norfolk, Lincolnshire and Yorkshire – areas which were far from land – a few feet of the so-called 'Red Chalk' was laid down. It is a brick-red, gritty limestone very rich in fossils.

Upper Cretaceous Times

In Britain all the earlier advances of the seas culminated in a final burst forward – westwards as far as Ireland. northwards to Scotland. Probably

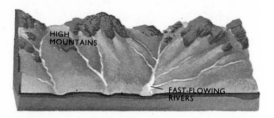

The strong streams from high land can carry large quantities of coarse rock fragments.

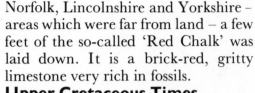

Low-lying land provides little or no sediment and this is thought to be the condition during the formation of the very pure chalk.

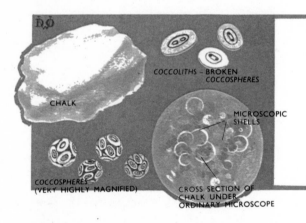

Under an ordinary microscope chalk can be seen to consist of fragments of broken shells set in a very fine-grained powder. The powder was long thought to be of inorganic origin – a mere ooze precipitated from the sea-water. But under the electron microscope the very fine particles could be seen to be the complete or broken skeletons of shelly algae. The complete skeletons

In the centre of the sea sticky, blue *Gault Clay* formed. It consists of very fine clay particles and is rich in fossils. Towards the shore-lines coarser rock fragments, brought from the land by rivers, still accumulated in shallower water, and are today called the *Upper Greensand*. The name is more appropriate for this sediment is mostly sandy and coloured green by glauconite. In

only the highest peaks of present Wales, Scotland and the Lake District remained above the surface of the water. Chalk was no doubt formed over the entire region but today has been largely removed by erosion.

The earliest chalk sediment is greyish in colour and contains up to 50% of silt and other impurities. Slowly the seas cleared and the chalk became steadily whiter and purer. Fossils of echinoids, crinoids, brachiopods, ammonites and molluscs are known. The land masses surrounding the sea must have been almost flat and unable to provide much sediment. In N.E. Ireland and West Scotland however, coarse sandstone is known to be of Upper Cretaceous age and these deposits must represent localized areas near the shorelines. Rivers must have flowed gently from the land into the Upper Cretaceous sea, however, for a constant supply of calcium carbonate was essential for the great thicknesses of chalk to form.

In the uppermost chalk, bands of flint (glassy silica, SiO_2) occur. Probably they are made from the silica of Cretaceous sponge skeletons dissolved at a later date by percolating water. This silica then re-solidified about

are called *coccospheres*, the broken fragments are called *coccoliths*.

Close relatives of these Cretaceous algae are found today at depths of only 600 feet. The Cretaceous sea therefore was probably never very deep and the purity of the chalk is thought due to a very small supply of weathered rock fragments from the flat desert lands of the time.

fossils or simply formed irregular-shaped lumps (nodules).

Cretaceous North America

As in Britain the Cretaceous Period brought to North America a last great submergence. Although both the Atlantic and Gulf coasts were invaded by the sea the main scene of inundation was the Rocky Mountain geosyncline. Right from the start of

the period the sea advanced over it from both the north and the south. Eventually these two inlets met and, hemmed in by highlands to the west, the water began to spread eastwards until in Late Cretaceous time North America was half submerged. A

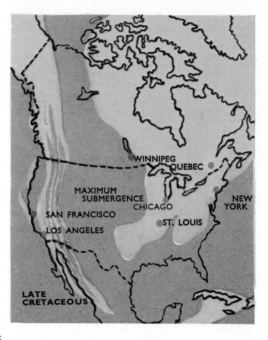

thousand mile wide stretch of water divided the continent right down the middle into two distinct parts, a broad, low eastern section and a narrow, rugged western section.

West of the Rocky Mountain geosyncline the mountains created during the preceding period continued to broaden and rise intermittently. Streams and rivers working apace with the rising land poured vast amounts of debris into the neighbouring depression, thus adding to the material from which the Rockies were to be born.

The closing stages of the Mesozoic Era were marked by growing crustal unrest which came to a climax in the second great phase of the Alpine Revolution, the *Laramide Orogeny* (mountain building is termed *orogenesis*). The vast quantities of rock which had accumulated in the great Rocky Mountain geosyncline were folded and faulted by tremendous forces until, out of the long depression which had been developing through the era and amid violent volcanic activity, the Rocky Mountain system was born, a great mountain range with a maximum width of 500 miles reaching right the way down North America. Although the Rockies were to be eroded considerably and uplifted again in the succeeding era it was this orogeny which determined their basic structure. The vast amount of material poured into the old geosyncline during this single period may be seen from the fact that Cretaceous formations reach the great thickness of 20,000 feet in Wyoming.

The Cenozoic
World

CHAPTER TWENTY-FIVE

The Tertiary Scene

GREAT changes in animal life mark the opening of the Tertiary period 70 million years ago. The age of reptile dominance was over. Not a single species of dinosaur is known to have survived from the previous Cretaceous period. The *ammonites* – a large group of squid-like molluscs that flourished in Jurassic and Cretaceous seas – had also disappeared. So had the *belemnites* – a group of molluscs very closely related to to-day's octopuses. What caused this mass extinction is unknown.

The new masters of the world were the mammals and birds. The mammals particularly increased in variety and became adapted to all sorts of surroundings.

Also increasing in number and variety were the molluscan snails and bivalves. The fossils of many forms still living today are preserved in Tertiary sediments, and these provide a method of dividing the Tertiary period into smaller units. The oldest

Scene in Eocene times. Luxuriant vegetation grew in the sub-tropical climate. Birds and mammals were the dominant animals.

division, the Palaeocene, contains very few fossils of modern molluscan species; the next, the Eocene, has slightly more, and the next, the Oligocene, has slightly more again. The fourth division is the Miocene in which the number of modern forms, though increased, is still less than the number of extinct forms. Finally, in the Pliocene division modern forms are more abundant than forms now extinct.

Tertiary Britain

Throughout most of Tertiary times the climate was warm. Luxuriant forests covered much of Britain and North-West Europe while in the seas warm water creatures flourished. The temperatures only began to drop at the start of the Ice Age in the following Quaternary period.

While Eocene sediments collected in Eastern England, vast quantities of basalt were flooding from volcanoes or through fissures in Antrim (Ireland) and the Inner Hebrides of Scotland. This volcanic rock forms the Giant's Causeway and Fingal's cave in the Isle of Staffa. Dating is made possible by plant remains recovered from associated sediments.
Molten material also cooled underground giving a variety of *igneous intrusions*.

At the start of *Eocene* times earth movements uplifted the sediments of North and West Britain. The rocks of Central England were tilted giving them their present eastward dip, while upwarping in the Wealden area started to form the Wealden anticline. The sea retreated to Eastern England and here in an area rarely extending further westwards than a line from the Wash to the Exe, Britain's Eocene sediment accumulated. Today this sediment is found preserved in two downwarped basins – one covering the London area and East Anglia, the other occupying parts of Hampshire, Sussex and Dorset. Originally the two areas were continuous though the early uplift of the Wealden anticline may have formed an island between them.

The first Eocene deposits (*Thanet Sands*) which are found in Kent and Essex consist of marine sands resting on top of flint nodules weathered from surrounding chalk land-masses.

Thereafter at any one moment in Eocene times two types of sediment were collecting. On the shores and along the coasts lagoonal muds accumulated while sands built up deltas; further eastwards, out to sea, there were deep-water sands and clays preserving marine fossils. Thus in the

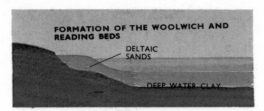

FORMATION OF THE WOOLWICH AND READING BEDS

DELTAIC SANDS

DEEP WATER CLAY

In Eocene times sandy deltas formed inshore while marine clays accumulated further out to sea.

FORMATION OF LONDON CLAY AND BAGSHOT BEDS

NEW DELTA FORMING (BAGSHOT SAND)

LONDON CLAY IN DEEP WATER

Invasion of the sea followed depositing marine clays. Inshore, shallow-water sands again started to accumulate.

London Basin the so-called *Woolwich and Reading* beds which follow the Thanet Sands, are marine in East Kent while further west, nearer the shore, they are freshwater and deltaic.

But to complicate matters the position of the Eocene shore-line was continually changing. An invasion westward of the sea would be followed by slow silting up inshore, causing the sea to retreat slowly once more to the

Britain in Eocene times. In Miocene times all of Britain was land.

BASALTS MAKING THE GIANT'S CAUSEWAY, N. IRELAND

IGNEOUS ROCKS EXTRUDED AT THE SURFACE

LAND

SEA

WEALDEN ISLAND

YELLOW PATCHES INDICATE WHERE TERTIARY ROCKS ARE FOUND TODAY

east. Thus the following *London Clay* represents an advance of the sea upon the land. It was formed in shallow water and contains marine fossils and also the remains of land plants and animals carried off the land by rivers. But westward, at the same time, the deltaic *Bagshot Sands* began to form, pushing slowly eastward, driving the sea back. In strong contrast to the heavy London Clays, the sands form high, well drained heath lands and pinewood country.

The oldest Eocene rocks in the Hampshire Basin are equivalent in age to the Woolwich and Reading beds of the London Basin. They are freshwater clays which probably formed in a lagoon. As in the London Basin invasion of the sea followed and London Clay was laid down offshore while Bagshot Sands with fossilized land plants formed inshore. The Eocene rocks in the London Basin do not appear to be complete, for two further invasions of the sea are recorded in the sediments of the Hampshire Basin.

Oligocene rocks occur only in the Hampshire Basin. If they were laid down in the London region they have since been eroded away. The Hampshire sediment consists of 650 feet of sands, clays and thin limestone. The shoreline was continually oscillating backwards and forwards, for marine

Sediment rapidly accumulated building a delta out into the water and causing the sea to retreat.

Top, *A wave-cut platform of a present-day shore.* Middle, *Wave-cut platform high on the North Downs cut by the Pliocene sea.* Bottom, *Distribution of land and sea in Pliocene times.*

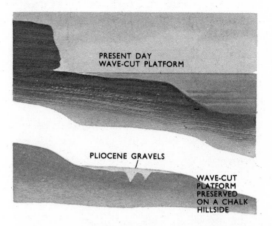

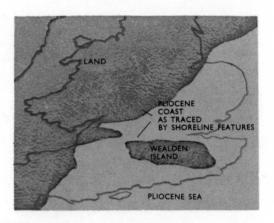

and freshwater deposits are present.

During *Miocene* times great earth movements uplifted the Alps and many other great mountain chains. But Britain was on the fringe of the unstable area and only gentle folding and faulting took place. This included the completion of the Wealden anticline in South-East England which probably commenced to form earlier, in Eocene times.

No Miocene rocks are known in Britain. They exist in France and other parts of the continent and probably Britain was part of the land mass providing the sediment.

By *Pliocene* times the sea again covered Southern and Eastern England. The land was some 700 feet lower, in relation to sea level, than it is

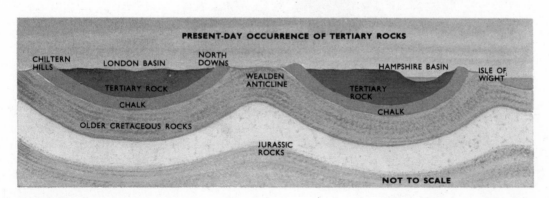

Tertiary sediments have been preserved in two downwarps of the crust (synclines). On high ground they have been removed by weathering.

today. In Southern England, only the crest of the Wealden anticline stood out of the water.

Since then, the land has been re-uplifted, but spectacularly preserved are low platforms cut into the chalk hills by the Pliocene seas. Today these platforms – once at sea level – are found at heights of 600 feet and more. In many places the platform is backed by a steep rise of slope, former cliffs that stood along the ancient shoreline.

Shoreline features are particularly well preserved on the northward slopes of the North Downs and along the southern slopes of the Chiltern Hills. The platforms are, in places, still coated with Pliocene marine sands and gravels.

More substantial Pliocene sediments are found forming part of the so-called *Crags* of East Anglia. Crags are shelly sandstones formed near the shorelines. The bottom-most *Coralline Crag* contains warm water Pliocene fossils but the following Red Crags have fossils of colder water creatures and are now usually taken to represent the first sediments of the Quaternary (Ice Age) period.

THE ISTHMUS OF PANAMA – LAND BRIDGE FOR INVADING PLACENTAL MAMMALS AT THE BEGINNING OF PLIOCENE TIMES (10 MILLION YEARS AGO)

THYLACOSMILUS — A SABRE-TOOTHED MARSUPIAL

SOUTH AMERICA, LIKE AUSTRALIA, WAS A STRONGHOLD OF MARSUPIAL MAMMALS – UNTIL PLACENTAL MAMMALS WERE ABLE TO INVADE

NOTOCYNUS

BORHYAENA

In early Tertiary times, 60 million years ago, South America was cut off from North America. Inside this great continent, marsupial (pouched) mammals flourished. The re-establishment of a land bridge 10 million years ago enabled the placental mammals that had evolved in North America, to invade. In the face of this competition most South American marsupials have become extinct.

Tertiary North America

The Atlantic and Gulf coasts were covered by sea for much of the Cenozoic. The rocks of this region are mainly sands, clays and chalky marls, extending two hundred miles or so inland. The Mississippi river was in existence in the Palaeocene, for the rocks of the western Gulf coast are non-marine and contain much lignite (low grade coal). Obviously the river and its tributaries maintained a swamp area there. Great thicknesses of Cenozoic deposits in the Gulf of Mexico indicate that this region was sinking slowly as the Mississippi brought down its sediment. Further south in Central America, however, the land was rising and late Cenozoic sediments are thin or missing.

By the end of the Mesozoic, the Appalachian region in eastern U.S.A. was an almost flat plain (*peneplain*).

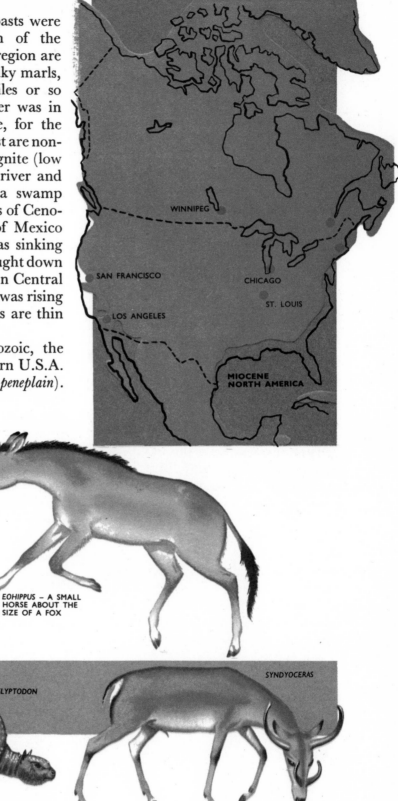

WINNIPEG

SAN FRANCISCO

CHICAGO

ST. LOUIS

LOS ANGELES

MIOCENE
NORTH AMERICA

EOHIPPUS – A SMALL
HORSE ABOUT THE
SIZE OF A FOX

GLYPTODON

SYNDYOCERAS

113

During the Cenozoic this region gradually rose up to form the present Appalachian mountains. There was no severe folding, for resistant rocks still show the original flat surface although they have been uplifted several thousand feet. Erosion of the softer rocks and intermittent uplift have helped to create the complex scenery of the mountains.

The *Laramide Orogeny* at the end of the Mesozoic lifted the Rocky Mountains into a rugged region. Several 'basins' were left between the peaks and these filled up with sediment so that by Oligocene times the region

of rapid soil erosion. The Grand Canyon, too, results from Cenozoic uplift causing the Colorado river to cut down through thousands of feet of rock.

The Pacific coast was subjected to various uplifts and submergences during the Cenozoic but at no time did the sea cover extensive areas. Thick terrestrial deposits accumulated in troughs surrounding the Sierra Nevada mountains which were rising at the time.

Volcanic activity was important during the Cenozoic Era. The earth movements associated with the Lara-

FLAT-TOPPED APPALACHIAN HILLS

was quite flat, the mountains worn down and buried in their own material. Later uplifts caused rivers to cut down and re-excavate the basins and to produce the present form of the mountains. The summits still show remnants of the flat Oligocene surface. Much of the material removed during the early erosion was deposited on the plains to the east of the mountains. Some of this remains as the High Plains but the rest has been eroded to some degree. The clays and sands have often developed into *badlands* because

mide orogeny died down in the Eocene, but in Miocene times renewed movements arose and continued on and off until the Pleistocene. Large areas of Columbia are covered with volcanic lava and in other places river cliffs show several successive lava flows.

The climate during the early Cenozoic was warm, even in the north (as shown by the presence of various fossil plants). Gradually however it cooled until, in Pleistocene times, the Great Ice Age began.

CHAPTER TWENTY-SIX

The Quaternary Scene

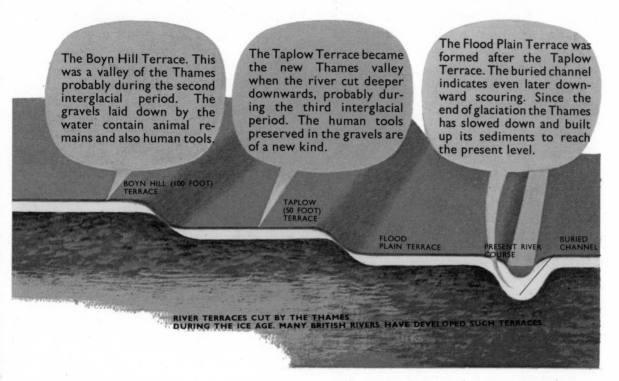

The Boyn Hill Terrace. This was a valley of the Thames probably during the second interglacial period. The gravels laid down by the water contain animal remains and also human tools.

The Taplow Terrace became the new Thames valley when the river cut deeper downwards, probably during the third interglacial period. The human tools preserved in the gravels are of a new kind.

The Flood Plain Terrace was formed after the Taplow Terrace. The buried channel indicates even later downward scouring. Since the end of glaciation the Thames has slowed down and built up its sediments to reach the present level.

BOYN HILL (100 FOOT) TERRACE

TAPLOW (50 FOOT) TERRACE

FLOOD PLAIN TERRACE

PRESENT RIVER COURSE

BURIED CHANNEL

RIVER TERRACES CUT BY THE THAMES DURING THE ICE AGE. MANY BRITISH RIVERS HAVE DEVELOPED SUCH TERRACES

A MILLION years or so is all that separates the close of Tertiary times from the present-day. This time interval is occupied by the so-called Quaternary period. Despite its shortness (the Cambrian period for instance, lasted 100 million years) a remarkable amount of geological study has been devoted to the thin, unhardened Quaternary sediments. There are two major reasons for this.

The Quaternary period is divided into a long *Pleistocene* interval and a very short *Holocene* interval.

Pleistocene time included the glacial episode which occupies most of the Quaternary period. Holocene time is made up of the last few thousand years since the retreat of the ice.

First, the world's last great ice age started at the beginning of Quaternary times; second, a curious mammal emerged, physically insignificant but mentally surpassing every other creature. This was Man.

In the Alpine region of Southern Europe, four separate ice advances during the Quaternary period have been recognized. The advances are separated by milder *interglacial* spells. Similarly, in Britain and North America four advances can be identified, though it is not certain that they exactly correspond with the four Alpine glaciations.

Finding evidence for glaciations in the sediments is very difficult for often the earlier glacial deposits have been swept away in the later glacial

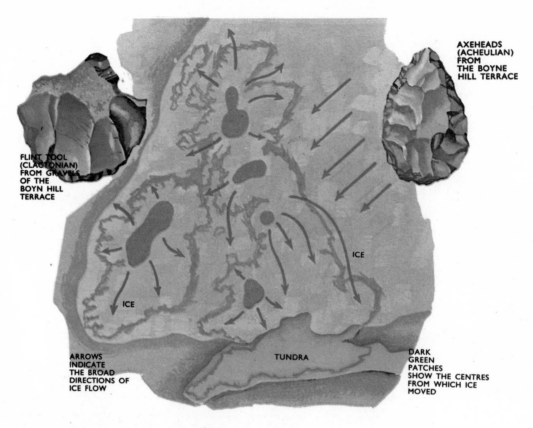

The second ice advance. The Cotswold and Chiltern Hills acted as
fenders and prevented further ice movement southwards.

episodes. Fortunately there is other
evidence available – the effect the ice
had on our present land form.

The Great Ice Age

The Quaternary period opened with
most of Britain standing out of the
water. South-east England was connected to the Continent and the River
Thames flowed westward into the
River Rhine. Parts of East Anglia
were still under the present North Sea
and sandy sediment formed here
(known as the *Red Crag*) contains many
cold-water fossils. This is the first sign
in Britain of a colder climate. Beneath
the Red Crag lie sediments of Tertiary
age containing fossils of a sub-tropical
climate.

The cold became severer. Glaciers

began to spread southward from the
highland in Scandinavia. They crossed
the North Sea and reached eastern
parts of Britain. But before they could
travel further, the climate changed.
Milder interglacial weather set in. The
ice thawed and the glaciers retreated
northwards. In the north of Norfolk,
thick deposits of *boulder clay* containing
many large rock fragments were left
behind by the ice. Rivers of water
which thawed from the glaciers, flowed
southward and deposited sands and
gravels in Hertfordshire. In the south
of Norfolk the sea again contained
warmer water animals.

Evidence of the second ice advance
is more complete. Apart from glacial
deposits in East Anglia, there are also

LEVALLOISIAN ARTIFACT FROM THE TAPLOW TERRACE

ICE

ICE

TUNDRA

The fourth and final ice advance – not so extensive as the second and third advances, but responsible for sculpturing much of our present land form.

sediments left by the ice in the English Midlands and the Severn Valley. The ice caps this time spread from high ground in Scotland, Wales and northern England. Glaciation became very extensive, the ice sheets reaching as far south as London. The following interglacial episode lasted a very long time and it is called the *Great Interglacial*. Freshwater deposits of the time are preserved in hollows in East Anglia. The sediment contains pollen grains which show that oaks, elms and hazels were the dominant trees. River gravels elsewhere contain remains of the warmth-loving hippopotamus and elephant. There are also man-made flint tools.

The third glacial episode was also

Pollen grains are often all that have been preserved of past trees. Pictures of how vegetation changed with changing climates can be built up.

PINE

OAK

BIRCH

ASH

extensive. Again, glacial deposits are found in East Anglia, the English Midlands and the Severn Valley. But the fourth ice advance was much more limited. Most of the English Midlands were free of ice. However in Scotland, Northern England and Wales where

The dumping of rock fragments by melting glaciers dammed rivers. Lakes were formed and eventually overflowed in other directions. Thus the River Severn once flowed northwards to the Irish Sea. Today, due to ice action, it has adopted a curious semi-

Warmer weather in an interglacial episode. Hippopotamus and elephant roamed the land. So did Man and he left behind many of his tools.

the glaciers were present, spectacular sculpturing of the land form took place. Ice movement gouged out hollow corries in steep hillsides, it refashioned valleys giving a characteristic U-shape to the previously V-shaped outline.

circular channel and flows out through the Bristol Channel.

The Ice Age in North America

In North America two distinct ice sheets are recognised, though they were almost certainly continuous for most of the time. One of these radiated from the Hudson Bay area, the other from the Cordilleran region. It is probable that over large areas the ice was as much as ten thousand feet thick, and, at its maximum extent, reached as far south as the Ohio River.

As in Europe, conditions were not mon interglacials. And as in Europe the glaciers played a vital part in shaping the modern scenery over much of the continent. Some seventy-five feet of soil and rock were stripped from the plains of Canada and plastered down further south to create

Tundra in Southern England during an ice advance. Arctic animals – mammoth, bear and woolly rhinoceros – were the chief inhabitants.

the same throughout the Great Ice Age: again there were four main periods of ice advance – the Nebraskan, Kansan, Illinoian and Wisconsin ice ages – separated by interglacial periods when the ice sheets retreated – the Aftonian, Yarmouth and Sanga-

the now fertile farmland of north-central U.S.A.; the Canadian shield was gouged into innumerable hollows now occupied by lakes; drainage patterns were radically altered by melt-waters flowing from the ice; and the Great Lakes were created.

In North America the ice radiated from two main centres, the Hudson Bay area and the Cordilleran region.

Dating the Great Ice Age

The use of radio-carbon dating has thrown some light on the actual ages of Pleistocene deposits, but, apart from those of the fourth glaciation and later, there is no great accuracy. Examination of the amount of weathering of old boulder clays has also helped to date the interglacial periods, but, without being sure that weathering proceeded at the same pace then as now, one cannot get more than a rough estimate. We do know, however, that the second interglacial period was far longer than the others and occupied, in fact, about one third of the Pleistocene.

American scientists have used the radio-carbon technique to study the fourth glaciation in the U.S.A. This method relies on the fact that living organisms contain a fixed proportion of carbon-14, the radioactive isotope of carbon. Gradually the radio-activity is lost and the proportion remaining is an indication of the time that has elapsed since the death of the organism. Drift deposits (i.e. boulder clays) contain many tree trunks that were presumably overwhelmed by the ice on its forward journey. When the ice melted, peat started to form on the wet land. Counts of radioactivity in these materials have provided some fairly accurate information about the last glaciation. The ice-cap reached its southern

A map showing the greatest probable extent of the Pleistocene Ice Caps in the Northern Hemisphere.

GÜNZ
NEBR
ICE A

AUSTRALOPIT
(AFRICA)

limit about 20,000 years ago, when its edge was in the region of Cincinnati in the state of Ohio. Warmer conditions then melted the ice and the glacier retreated. During the retreat there were numerous temporary re-advances but the ice finally left the Great Lakes about 8,000 years ago, geologically speaking very recently. The ice cap had disappeared from Britain long before this and it is interesting to note that Eastern U.S.A. still suffers far more severe winters than European countries of the same latitude.

The Future?

The time that has elapsed since the last retreat of the ice is relatively short and it is quite possible that we are in another interglacial period. Greenland and Antarctica still support large ice-caps which would re-advance upon a slight change in climate.

On the other hand, if the Ice Age is over and the world is returning to a more normal state (assuming that for most of its history there were no glaciers), the ice may disappear completely. The oceans would then rise

Connected with the Ice Age are several features showing that the levels of land and sea were continuously changing. Examples are the raised beaches and sunken forests about our shores and the successive river terraces associated with many of our rivers. Raised beaches and sunken forests are caused by a change of the sea level relative to the land. But there is no simple explanation. A combination of two factors is more likely. First, during the inter-glacial period more water would be released by melted ice, causing a rise in sea-level. Second, the weight of advancing glaciers probably pushed the land down so that the sea-level appeared to rise. Any upward movement of the land also caused the rivers to cut downwards. Their earlier valleys are left as terraces high above the new river level. Careful work on such geographical features has helped geologists to trace the history of the Ice Age.

Diagrammatic representation of the Pleistocene glacials and inter-glacials.

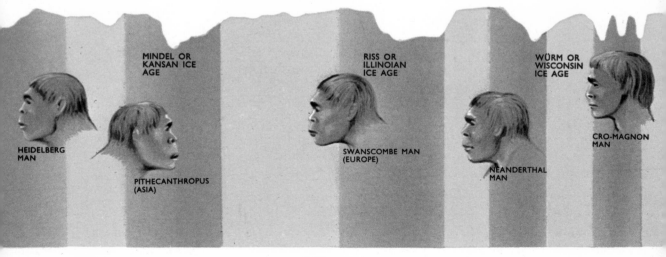

MINDEL OR KANSAN ICE AGE

RISS OR ILLINOIAN ICE AGE

WÜRM OR WISCONSIN ICE AGE

HEIDELBERG MAN

PITHECANTHROPUS (ASIA)

SWANSCOMBE MAN (EUROPE)

NEANDERTHAL MAN

CRO-MAGNON MAN

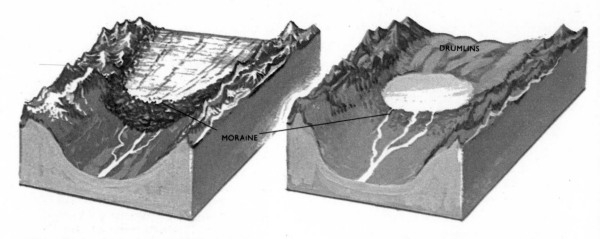

The effects of glaciation. Valley glaciers produce U-shaped valleys. (Left) A stationary glacier snout forming a moraine. (Right) The valley after the glacier has melted. A lake is dammed up by the moraine. Boulder clay and large rocks cover the valley floor.

by about one hundred feet and many of our cities would be lost.

Whichever way future events may turn, the causes of glaciation will always be subjects for discussion. The occurrence of earlier ice-ages suggests a rhythmic pattern but one with a very long period. Periodic variations in the Earth's orbit affect climate but if they alone were responsible there would have been a great many ice-ages. We are aware of sunspot cycles and how they affect the Sun's radiation. It may be that there are longer cycles that produce more severe effects. This is perhaps the best hypothesis, but none, of course, can be proved right or wrong.

The Holocene Epoch

Since the end of the last glacial episode, about 15,000 years ago, sediments of less spectacular nature have been forming. Hidden by the sea, marine sands and muds have continued to accumulate, and on land, sediments are forming in lakes and rivers. Man himself with his dumps and rubbish tips has become an agency of deposition. One particularly important geological event has been the final cutting of the land bridge which united Britain with the rest of Europe.

Glaciers did not just flow in a north-south direction. Their movements are far more complex. Something of the paths followed by the ice can be discovered by studying the rock fragments in the boulder clays — the *indicator erratics*. Rock fragments from the first boulder clays of East Anglia can be matched with outcrops from Scandinavia for instance.

CHAPTER TWENTY-SEVEN

Archaeology and the Scientist

THE archaeologist reconstructs the lives and activities of past peoples – how they made a living, what tools they used, what skills they had acquired, even what diseases afflicted them and what beliefs they had. The clues for building up these pictures are the traces such peoples have left

By identification of minerals in building stones and stone implements the geologist can often trace where the original rock came from. Some of the stones from Stonehenge, for instance, are traced to Pembrokeshire.

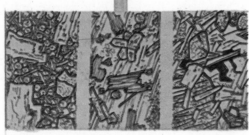

behind – bones, tools, ornaments, pottery, buildings.

In his work, the archaeologist is assisted by a whole range of scientists – geologists, zoologists, botanists, chemists, physicists. Specialized scientific knowledge reveals information from the most unlikely sources.

Human and Animal Remains

The fractured bones of fallen war-riors may reveal just what types of weapon were used in past warfare. Even the methods of fighting can be reconstructed. Diseases may also leave their mark on the skeleton – leprosy and tuberculosis for example. Rickets, a malformity of the bones, is very easily diagnosed; it is caused by lack of Vitamin D and a prevalence of rickets in a past community suggests a low standard of nutrition.

The teeth of past peoples may reveal something of their diet. Predominant meat-eaters rarely have rotten teeth. As the quantity of grain in the diet rises there is an overall tendency for tooth-decay.

Bones of animals may often be found associated with human communities, and their identification usually goes a long way to establishing the staple human diet. The remains may be of animals known to move from pasture to pasture – reindeer and bison, for instance. Almost certainly the human community also led a wandering existence.

Sometimes the bones may be of domestic animals. Domestic animals do not lead the rugged competitive lives of their wild counterparts and consequently there may be modifications in their skeletons. For instance, the places for muscle attachment on the bones became smaller. Bones supply other evidence that a community had taken up domesticating animals. A high proportion of bones belonging to young animals is not likely to be found in a hunting society, where the larger, adult animals were

A chip of rock removed for study is replaced by coloured plaster. The shape and appearance of the implement is retained.

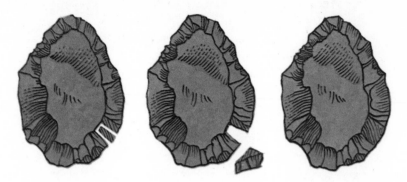

sought for food. A high proportion of female sheep bones suggests that the females were kept for milking.

Stones and Pottery

By cutting through sections of rocks and examining them with a microscope, the geologist is able to identify all the minerals present. Often peculiarities in the proportions of minerals or oddities in their position and

Some archaeological sites are obvious – ruins and earth-works for instance. Other sites may show up clearly in aerial photographs or be discovered by accident. Before planning the excavation of a site, further information may be obtained by measuring the electrical resistivity of the ground with special meters. Minerals making rocks and soils give a high resistance to an electric current but moisture (containing dissolved salts) improves the conductivity.

Solid archaeological structures and places where soil has been previously distributed gives variety to water-holding capacity. This variety can often be detected by differences in resistivity readings.

structures make it possible to find out the origin of the rock – the exact outcrop where the sample came from.

In the past, tools and buildings were often made from hard rock. In identifying the source of the rocks the geologist can also discover something of past industry and communication. Four thousand years ago, for instance, stone hand axes were employed by the peoples of Britain. These specimens can generally be traced to one of the four 'factories' – Cornwall, North Wales, the Lake District and Ulster.

Similarly, sections of pottery can be examined under the microscope. The clay minerals, together with material added to decrease shrinkage (the filler), can be identified. Sometimes, from the nature of filler or clay, it is possible to say whether pottery was locally made or brought into a region.

Metal Objects

Metal implements gradually succeeded those made of stone. Microanalytical techniques such as flame photometry and spectography reveal just what metals were alloyed together. Because the samples needed are so small, little or no damage is done to the object. One technique devised enables metals to be analysed without even extracting a sample.

The surfaces of metal objects can be examined with microscopes and X-rays. The appearance and structure of the crystals of metal show whether articles were cast into moulds or hammered from sheets and solid lumps. The crystals also may show how different components were joined together, even how repairs were

of absolutely dating objects. This is the carbon-14 method. Most carbon atoms have an atomic weight of 12. But cosmic radiation striking the atmosphere forms another variety of carbon – a radioactive form with an atomic weight of 14. Some of the radioactive form is absorbed by plants as carbon dioxide. Animals absorb carbon-14 by eating the plants. When organisms die, no more carbon

A pattern of good and bad summers is recorded by the width of the annual rings in long-living trees. Patterns in preserved pieces of wood may be related to this 'calendar' and the exact age of the wood is revealed.

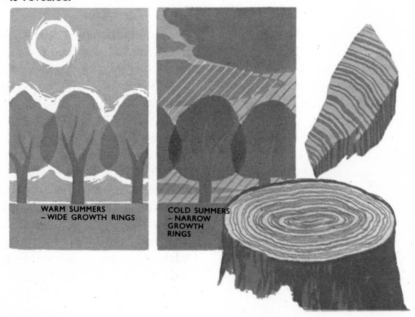

WARM SUMMERS – WIDE GROWTH RINGS

COLD SUMMERS – NARROW GROWTH RINGS

carried out.

Making the Archaeological Calendar

There are two types of dating for an archaeological find. One gives the exact age of the object – how old it is in terms of years (*absolute dating*). The other determines the age of an object in relationship to other objects (*relative dating*).

The nuclear physicist has provided the archaeologist with the best way

is absorbed. The radioactive carbon that has been taken in decays, breaking down to form nitrogen. The rate of the breakdown is constant. After 5,568 years, half the radioactive carbon has decayed; after another 5,568 half as much again has disappeared. By measuring the quantity of radioactive carbon left in old wood, bones, peat, antlers, grain and charcoal, the quantity that has decayed can be approximately estimated together

The quantity of fluorine absorbed by bones, may reveal the relative ages of the remains. The skull of Swanscombe Man from Kent, has been proved to be of great antiquity. Confirmatory tests can be made by measuring the quantities of uranium and nitrogen the bones contain.

with the time this has taken.

In America, botanists have established an absolute time scale going back to 1000 B.C. Annual rings of trees vary in width according to past seasonal climates. Distinct wood patterns due to climatic changes are apparent. In dry climates wood used in the buildings of old civilizations is often preserved. The wood can be dated by comparison with sections of tree trunks.

For relative dating the archaeologist has developed methods of his own – for instance tools can be relatively dated according to their style and efficiency. Just as a modern jet aircraft is obviously a later development than a biplane, so can one type of tool in a region be dated later than another.

Botanists and chemists provide alternative methods. Botanists employ pollen grains. Unless Man interferes the sequence of pollen accumulating in a region will reflect climatic changes. Since the close of the Ice Age, the weather has become warmer. In many places, arctic plants were followed by sub-arctic plants, then temperate plants. Gradually the forests evolved into those of modern times. Archaeological remains may be found in places where considerable pollen is present. The age of the remains can then be related to the climatic scale. Sometimes, by radioactive dating of the pollen, even an absolute date of the remains may be possible.

Chemists have contributed methods which involve measuring small quantities of either uranium, fluorine, or nitrogen in bone. Over long periods of time, bones and teeth buried in the ground slowly absorb traces of fluorine and uranium. The quantity depends upon how much is present in a given regional area, and the sort of water circulation there. Fragments taken from the same regions can be relatively dated according to the quantities they have absorbed.

Nitrogen is present in bone as bone protein. Fresh bones contain about 4-5% nitrogen. This quantity is reduced as the protein decays. The rate of decay will depend upon surrounding physical chemical and bacteriological conditions.

Index

DATE DUE

DE 2 '69			
MY 17 '71			
AG 30 '72			
SE 14 '72			
OC _ 7 '75			
MAY 29			
GAYLORD			PRINTED IN U.S.A.